Distance Training

Photos with kind support of

Arthur Lydiard/ Garth Gilmour

Distance Training
for Masters

Meyer & Meyer Sport

British Library Cataloguing in Publication Data
A catalogue record for this book is available from the British Library

Lydiard, Arthur/
Distance Training for Masters
Lydiard, Arthur ; Gilmour, Garth.
– Oxford : Meyer & Meyer Sport (UK) Ltd., 2000
ISBN 1-84126-018-5

© 2000 by Meyer & Meyer Sport (UK) Ltd
Oxford, Aachen, Olten (CH), Vienna,
Québec, Lansing/ Michigan, Adelaide, Auckland, Johannesburg, Budapest
e-mail: verlag@meyer-meyer-sports.com
Photos: Neil's Shipper
(showing 1960 Olympic marathon bronze medalist Barry Magee)
Cover photo: Neil's Shipper
Cover design: Birgit Engelen, Stolberg
Cover and Type exposure: frw, Reiner Wahlen, Aachen
Editorial: John Coghlan
Typesetting: Quay
Printed and bound in Germany by
Burg Verlag Gastinger GmbH, Stolberg
ISBN 1-84126-018-5

CONTENTS

Arthur Lydiard

1 FOREWORD

Before New Zealander Arthur Lydiard became recognised as the world's finest middle and distance running coach, and the guru of the international cult of jogging for fitness, the 42-kilometre marathon race was the haunt of athletes regarded, with a mixture of affection and ridicule, as nut-cases. Runners who could not make an impression over any other distance, clapped-out six-milers, plodders, lunatics. Marathons were as few and far between as the runners who took part in them. The times they recorded were mostly indifferent by today's standards because few in their right mind trained specifically to run them any better. Women marathoners did not exist at all.

New Zealand can lay claim to one of the first marathons run in the world – certainly the southernmost, since it was held in the far south of the country's South Island – on July 14, 1909, soon after Dorando Pietri's sensational finish in the 1908 Olympic marathon in London. The oldest is the famous Boston run which began in 1897. In New Zealand's second marathon, the winner was a professional, and there were questions about the accuracy of course measurements, timekeeping and general supervision. The third, better controlled and with ten starters, was won in 2:58.23.

To indicate how slowly the times came down over the following years, in the 1950 Commonwealth Games in Auckland, New Zealand, three New Zealanders finished in 2:40 or just over. One of them was Arthur Lydiard. Four years later, Lydiard broke 2:40 for the first time. He was then 37 years old and beginning to fire his training system into a growing band of young runners who provided the raw material for his subsequent dominance of middle and distance running world-wide.

In 1962, jogging was born in New Zealand as a get-fit, stay-fit regime. Lydiard's dominant athletes, led by Peter Snell, Murray Halberg and Barry Magee, demonstrated the arts, skills and rewards of running to their countrymen and women, and it became easy to raise the awareness that systematic running or jogging could be good for you, fun for you and satisfying for you.

Mass fun-running, and its almost logical extension marathon running, took off around the world soon after. Suddenly, tens of thousands of men and women were running the distance, with fields so packed that all but the gun runners off the front spent their first kilometres at little more than a shuffle until they thinned out and found enough room to begin extending their strides.

More significantly, the bulk of those huge fields have always been masters runners. Many began as keep-fit joggers who became so fit that the dormant instinct to compete and to reach for personal goals roared back into action. For people learning and succeeding to run well, it became a logical challenge to complete a 10-kilometres fun run or race, then a half-marathon and then that ultimate, a full marathon, to see how far and how fast they could go. The original intention, merely to run regularly for their health's sake, escalated into today's mass-start marathons all around the globe.

In Auckland, a fun run round the city's eastern shoreline road started with 1,200, most of them joggers, and blossomed until, within a decade, 80,000 men, women and children poured in a sweating mass that blocked the road for more than two kilometres.

Just as the early marathoners were branded as nut-cases, mainly by those who could not possibly have "footed" it with them, the couch potatos of today still regard as nutters the men and women of all ages, shapes and abilities who pound marathon courses with only two aims in mind – to get to the end and, if possible, set personal bests for their own satisfaction. What is not appreciated is that all these aging runners are making a huge contribution to their own well-being, their own futures and, if it could be quantified, to their countries' well-being as well.

It is a sad commentary on the modern world that, while millions of older people are taking to their feet to stay fit and healthy, modern youth, beguiled by television and computer, by fast food and car, is becoming progressively less and less fit, more and more obese. The youngster who walks upstairs when an elevator is available has become a rarity. So is the one who will eat fresh fruit when fried chips are around.

New Zealand research has shown that only half of 16- and 17-year-olds are getting more than 30 minutes of exercise each day. The rising level of obesity matches studies in America, Canada and Britain. Only 30 to 50 per cent of young people belong to sports clubs.

The research also found that young people with sedentary parents are twice as likely to be inactive as those with sporting parents.

This finding is another compelling reason for older people to get out and get fit — to light the signal fires for the younger generations that they are eating and idling their way to poor health and potentially early graves.

Before Lydiard, their fathers and grandfathers were possibly going the same way, although they did not have the freedom from exercise which end-of-century technology has brought. Most still had to push their lawn-mowers, cars were not two-a-penny and three-per-household as they are now; physical effort was required for many normal activities; and New Zealand had a tradition of out-door living.

Today, with the move towards computer-shopping, with carparks first priority for any new commercial or industrial development, with e-mail, cellphones and faxes eliminating the need to walk to shops, to post offices, to anywhere to do ordinary business, that effort is vanishing.

But jogging and its healthy, booming offshoots – half and full marathons, masters games, and other activities geared for the over-forties – are taking up and removing the slack which develops with lack of exercise. One side-effect, an awareness of the value of better eating habits, helps the fat to go along with the slack.

But why run? Because it is the easiest thing to do for starters, it knows neither sex nor age barriers, it is cheap in relativity to most other sports or physical activity, it is available at just about everybody's front door, and it works where the need is most important — on maintaining healthy heart, lungs and circulation systems.

It eases work stress, improves sleeping habits, sharpens mental activity. The first steps you take from your doorstep can lead to a better world.

Perhaps your first reaction to the thought of getting up and out running is: I cannot; that is not for me.

Consider a couple of case examples:
One is a young man, 27, raising a family of four, working sometimes at two jobs, playing rugby football for winter recreation, some swimming and track running in the summer. He did not train much. Like most of his age he thought he was fit because he was taking part.

He was inveigled into a six-mile (10 km) run with a friend who was an experienced distance runner. His pulse rate rose quickly, he gasped for air, his legs were rubbery. He was nowhere near as fit as he thought he was.

At this point he broke from the normal reaction. Instead of groaning until his racked muscles recovered and then forgetting the experience, he thought about what was happening to him. If this is what I am like at 27, he thought, what will I be like at 47? And what can I do about it? His conclusion: spasmodic dashing about on a football field had little effect, but the sustained run had affected his entire body to a marked degree. Therefore, if tackled properly with less impetuosity, it could be beneficial to general health. But why and how much?

This man was Arthur Lydiard and what he subsequently did to himself in seeking the answers to those questions might be considered obsessional. Perhaps it was, but the world should now be thankful because out of that obsession grew the world's finest middle and distance training technique and the international fitness cult of jogging.

In 1982, American athletic coach J. O. Hanna, in his book *Running with Your Head*, discussing the shift in training emphasis in the 1950s, said this: "The hat trick in this belongs to Arthur Lydiard. Runners coached by him dominated middle and long distances in the 1950s and 1960s; he has a decisive part in turning millions of people on to jogging and running; his initiatives began almost 30 years ago and they persist. No other human can claim more than a part of any of these three areas."

His training methods had, again, absolute success, as long as they were supervised by him or the very few who were fully acquainted with them.

Here again, only too many added and subtracted not only from his success story but also from his training methods.

"... Beginners, joggers, runners and racers as well as coaches and administrators were ignited by his enthusiasm and took the first step to benefit from his knowledge. But fewer took the second step and the numbers decreased with every additional step. And there were those who tried adapting his methods to their environment and many who got carried away by their efforts to improve his systems; some with temporary, some with lasting, but only too many without success.

However obvious or hidden, Lydiard's jogging, running and racing methods represent a large part of today's training programme. Its foundation is a total stamina period, followed by several phases of specific stress adaptation routines."

In short, what he was saying then – and it still applies today – is that the only way to full potential is the Lydiard Way.

The second case? He was a 36-year-old who was invited by Lydiard, among a group of athletes and officials, to try a simple squat. He tried. It was simple. But the others nearly killed themselves laughing when both his knees cracked like pistol shots. Arthur looked at him with a certain amount of pity then said, "But even you could run a marathon."

Some days later, the fellow went with Lydiard for his first run in about 16 years. Lydiard being thorough, he made the run a three-miler (nearly 5 km). To his companion it was about 110 per cent uphill. He blistered all but one of his toes, knotted, without exception, all his leg muscles, burned his lungs and took about a week to recover.

But he bought running shoes and tackled the problem with the idea of proving Lydiard wrong – to prove he could not run a marathon. It was hard and sometimes depressing and discouraging effort, fitted round long hours of work, but he began to realize he was getting more out of running than he had ever got out of anything else, especially his 60 to 80 a day cigarette habit.

He even tackled and conquered Lydiard's notorious Waiatarua training circuit, more than 35 km of steeply undulating road through a range of steep, bush-clad hills framing Auckland's western edge. The Halbergs and Snells cruised it in just over two hours, he staggered home after more than three. A few days later, when his body recovered, he felt the fittest he had ever felt.

And, four months after his knees cracked, he ran his first marathon. He proved Lydiard was right after all.

That runner was me, and Lydiard gave me a recipe for beating the mental and physical lethargy of working long hours, the ability to enjoy my other pursuits in life. He brought my pulse down from about 78 to 51 in those four months and it is still around 58, though I am now 73 and an inconsistent exerciser with knee problems which preclude jogging. But I can pedal a bike for hours and I play better golf than I ever did. Proof of another Lydiard dictum: that once you have got fit, you can maintain a level of fitness with much reduced effort.

This book explains how you can do it too.

Garth Gilmour   Auckland, New Zealand, 1999

2 THE VITAL REASON FOR RUNNING

Perhaps not everyone would want to live longer, but everyone would like to live fitter, free from customary illnesses, aches and pains, and the general deterioration that we accept will accompany the passing years.

Staying fit can be accomplished even at a late stage in life, simply by developing and maintaining a strong heart, sound lungs and a cardio vascular system that moves the blood supply efficiently through an exercise-expanded system to all corners of the body to feed well-toned muscles. The key is your ability to take up oxygen and use it efficiently.

It has been calculated that people who remain moderately active throughout life will still have a progressive decrease in lung capacity, from, say, an uptake of around 52 (in millilitres of air divided by body weight per minute) at age 20, down to 48 at 30, 44 at 40, 39 at 50 and 35 at 60. The decline is significant – but it need not happen at that rate. The human organism as it ages will inevitably lose some of its performance capacity, but it is possible – and thousands are now proving it – to positively slow down the rate of decline and even to turn it around. In some instances the ability to keep performing at a high level far beyond the accepted norm has been remarkable.

The days when active sportspeople signed off and retired to the TV couch when they were in their late twenties or early thirties are long gone. Today, the athlete in many sports merely steps, at 25 or 40 or 50, depending on his or her sporting activities' threshhold, into a whole new level of competitive activity – the masters. In golf, for instance, professionals reaching 50 and becoming "masters" enter a sphere in which, although they may play shorter courses and reduce the number of rounds they play, they can earn as much, if not more, than they did in the open fields. All they have to do is maintain a base of physical fitness on which to sustain their playing skills and they can confidently continue playing world-class golf for a living for another 15 or 20 years. There are those who have admitted that they look forward to their "masters" status because they know they will have the opportunity to earn more, and raise their standard of living.

Masters track and field athletes at the highest levels can now carry on international careers even when they have reached 80 years of age or more. They are no longer any threat to Olympic hopefuls but, in their own age-groups, they can set world records and win world titles that, not many decades ago, did not exist.

They sprint, they run distance, they hurdle, they throw the javelin, shot and discus, they pole-vault at equal levels with their peers from all over the world. They swim, they cycle, they contest triathlons and duathlons, and the degrees of ability they demonstrate are often remarkably high. Age does not seem to weary them.

This book explains how you can join those masters athletes.

3 THE BASIC SYSTEM

Just about anyone could walk or run or run/walk a marathon. It is not as great a distance at it may seem. All it needs is some careful thought, careful conditioning and careful preparation.

In the same way, my so-called marathon-type training system, which is based around running a controlled 160 km a week, with up to the same mileage again in supplementary jogging if the athlete has the time and the will, is equally achievable by far more people than you would imagine.

All my young athletes of the 50s, 60s and 70s used this formula to build their stamina and endurance. Whether they were 800 metres runners or marathoners, they used exactly the same conditioning method so that, on top of the superlative, near-tireless physical fitness that system established, I could build their specialist requirements of speed, sharpness, style and so on. Joggers who have gone on to become long-distance runners have followed the same guidelines.

With my system of phased training elements, I could aim ordinary runners – and Murray Halberg, Peter Snell, Barry Magee and my other top runners were very ordinary at the beginning of their careers – at the first major events they wanted to win and place them in those events at the peak of readiness.

I could then keep them at that peak for as long as was required for the rest of the season's campaign.

So, with a collection of runners who ranged over all distances, I was able to target the national titles from the half-mile to the marathon and win them all, year after year for more than a decade before I moved my coaching emphasis from individual New Zealand athletes to coaching coaches on an international scale and athletes everywhere, through national coaching contracts in various parts of the world, through seminars and coaching camps and clinics and through my books, which have now been in constant publication for nearly 40 years.

The technique I developed half a century ago still works as effectively today as long as no attempt is made to shortcut or modify it. These days, now that I am in my eighties, I confine my training activities to helping by correspondence and on the Internet, and to advising a few runners, young and old, who come to me. In recent years, I have helped the young ones to a considerable dominance of high school middle and distance events at local and national levels, and what they do as youngsters is little changed from what Halberg and Snell did when they were youngsters. Some of the older runners feature prominently in masters' events and produce quite startling times in doing so.

There is no sense in changing or fiddling with a proven system, any more than it is sensible to begin modifying a car engine that is producing top performance.

The point here is that what youngsters do to achieve their goals is no different from what you, as masters old enough to be their parents, or even their grand-parents, need to do to achieve any goals you choose to set yourselves.

And whether you are only now deciding that running or walking is an exercise you need to take up, or whether you are an established masters athlete, the programme is the same, once the preliminary groundwork of stamina-building has been done. I mention walking because this running-fit programme I have devised can be used for other sporting activities. You cannot become an efficient distance walker unless you have conditioned yourself properly by running. Running will help the golfer, the footballer or tennis player, the boxer or wrestler, the rower or kayaker, the hockey player or netballer, by building a platform of tirelessness on which the individual game skills and techniques can be better developed and more efficiently maintained.

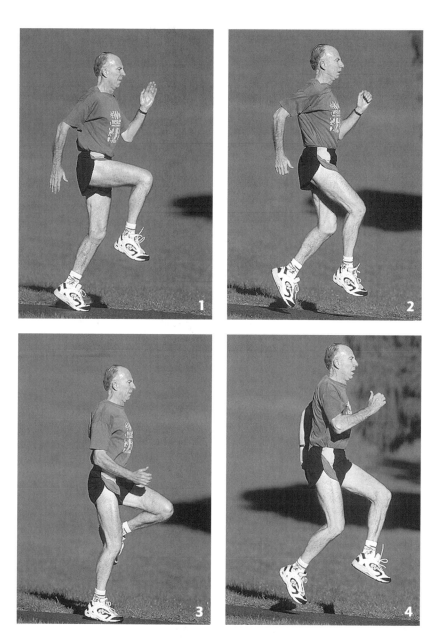

Magee demonstrates a high knees exercise, a bouncing action with relaxed, straight-through arm action.

Streching exercise, performed without strain.

4 STARTING FROM SCRATCH

If you have not run before, your first steps must be to your medical adviser. Explain what you want to do and how you intend to do it. Most doctors today recognise the need for physical activity and will encourage it, but you need to check for unsuspected conditions which might be harmful, even dangerous. Even children have been known to suffer from heart problems which could prove fatal during sudden vigorous exercise.

That done and the clearance given, equip yourself with the right kind of shoes to run in and the right clothing. I will discuss shoes in detail later because they are the vital connection between you and the ground you will be running over, and the wrong kind of shoes can lead to minor and serious problems.

Starting is simplicity itself. Run out for five minutes at an easy pace, turn and run home again. If you take longer than five minutes to get back because you cannot hold the pace, you have found your aerobic threshold, crossed it and moved into an anaerobic state. So, next run, ease back, aim to finish as you began.

When you have mastered that, extend your time out to, say, ten minutes each way, then to fifteen each way and so on. And the quickest way to see a sudden leap in ability is to follow the hard-easy, hard-easy system — every longer run must be followed by a shorter, easier one to enable your organism to adjust to the new demands being placed on it. Thus, you run fifteen minutes one day, five the next, then another fifteen, another five, until you feel ready for another extension. The effort must always be well within yourself. If you force yourself, your progress is more likely to be backwards; if you run with comfort, your development could be spectacular.

Be patient. Step up to 30 minutes, with two 15-minute days in between to give your body adequate time for recovery. Then try 45 minutes, again followed by two 15-minute days and, when you can handle that, run for an hour with two 15-minute days before the next hour. Then you can start to bring up the intermediate days – alternating an hour, two half-hours, an hour and so on.

Once you have mastered this you can extend that long run as you feel. This is the most effective way. Some try running 15 minutes every day, then 30 a day, then 45 a day. Okay, they can do it, but the way I recommend will achieve the fitness you seek three times faster. You cannot neglect those vital recovery days.

The world's first joggers were a bunch of about 20 Auckland, New Zealand, businessmen, most of whom had had mild heart attacks. They ranged in age from 40 up to 70-plus. Most of them could not run more than 100 metres at first but, within eight months, eight of them ran a full marathon. A 74-year-old who had had several heart attacks managed less than 50 metres on his first jog. Six months later, having shed 60 lb (27 kg) in weight, he ran 20 miles without stopping.

A friend who had done nothing before began running to my programme at 47. He was a huge man. He shed 27 kg in a year and, although still big, entered – and finished – a full triathlon, which meant swimming 2.5 km, cycling more than 160 km and finishing with a marathon.

These are not unusual cases. The world is full of men and women who, late in life, have discovered physical potential they never dreamed they possessed, simply because they conditioned themselves for it systematically by my simple method. All they needed were patience, dedication, the will to improve their lives and to have fun doing it.

When you start jogging, even if you go right back to the basic walk-a-lamppost jog-a-lamppost method before embarking on the routine I have outlined above, you will experience muscle soreness. This is caused by lactic acid build-up in muscles unaccustomed to being worked hard, and/or by the tearing of muscle tissue which has been gummed up through underuse. This is not a problem. You can use massage to ease the discomfort but you must get out and jog or run again the following day, even if the run is shorter or slower. You must stimulate your heart to push your blood around, raise the blood pressure and flush away the waste products which are causing the soreness. Your heart is the best massager you can use.

If you stop the exercise and wait for the muscle ache to go, you will be right back at the beginning again, setting yourself up for a repeat of the problem. You will have gained nothing.

You can help with hot baths, but an excellent and easy immediate treatment is to turn a cold hose on your legs as soon as you finish a run or, if a sea or lake is handy, go for a wade.

So there it is: begin easily, run through any muscle soreness, and spend a few weeks to get yourself from your backside to a point where you can run easy-paced for as long as you like once a week, and you have set the stage for being a true master.

Streching and warm-up exercises. Diagonal toe-touching, forward bend and

leg swinging.

Magee shows the ideal Lydiard style, relaxed upper body, arms low and moving parallel to running line, eliminating upper body sway and loss of forward momentum.

5 THE TECHNIQUE OF RUNNING

Running is simple. You merely begin moving at faster than a walk and you are jogging. Add more speed and you are running. But how you do this is important. Correct running style enables fast development and is a protection against the problems which can arise from bad running style.

We do not all run the same. Our body shapes vary, some have longer legs, shorter legs, wider hips, no hips and so on. Weights differ. All sorts of factors come into it. But we should all try to develop the correct technique because it is important to conserve energy for the act of running and make every movement as efficient as possible. Every sport has its correct ways and its wrong ways of doing the basics, and the nearer you can fit yourself to the correct way the better will be your performance.

Rowers and cyclists, for example, have to be concerned with correct seat adjustment, with getting the distances and leverages of arms and legs accurately set according to body weight and limb extensions. Golfers have a seemingly complicated system of checks and balances to get the swing right but, as in anything, once the basic principles of technique have been established and mastered, the application becomes comparatively simple.

The basics of good running ARE simple, although, if you want to delve deeper into the technicalities, England's former national coach, Geoffrey Dyson, put it all perfectly in his book, *The Mechanics of Athletics*, first published more than three decades ago.

The raw recruit to the art of running may progress initially at a moderately fast shuffle, on bent legs with the feet hardly off the ground; the expert practitioner uses a high knee lift and drives off a straight back leg. In between lies a lot of patient controlled practice.

The knee lift is the key to running properly. The knees must come up so that the thigh is as near horizontal as possible and the feet should lift high behind. This shortens the lever established by the knee, and it is indisputable that the short lever will move faster than the long one. A foot coming through low to the ground produces a slow stride; a foot coming through high gives a fast stride.

Hold one end of a pencil and move it to and fro, then do the same with a three-foot ruler. Which is easier to move faster?

Watch sprinters training or warming-up. They always include a high, bouncing knee exercise, fast, fast, fast, bringing the knees up, bang, bang, bang, with the heels hitting the butt. Interestingly, as a demonstration of physiological differences, the average Caucasian cannot get his knees up high while holding his hips back and leaning his body forward, as the Negro can. So he has to learn to run upright.

The upper body and arms play little part in running. You should run as you walk, with the arms loose and relaxed and moving in a straight line. The elbow flexes naturally and the hand moves through to brush past the thigh. Do not clench your fists, as we see many runners doing. Bunched fists, or carrying hand-weights with the idea that it will help, are classic examples of doing it wrongly. The shoulder muscles tighten and tightened shoulder muscles lead to shoulder roll. And shoulder roll means the runner is throwing his weight from side to side and interfering with his primary object, which is to go straight ahead with the least possible effort.

Do not let anyone tell you that improved upper body strength, or the strange exercise of furious arm pumping while standing still, will make you run faster. The only target worth pursuing is to make the legs run faster. Your arm movements will co-ordinate naturally whenever you change stride or speed. But you cannot make your arms control what your legs are doing.

Two of my finest runners, Murray Halberg and Lasse Viren, were proof that upper body strength is totally unnecessary for running. A football injury left Halberg with a withered left shoulder and arm, which he could not use, so he simply tucked it in at his side and still ran with beautiful balance and ease. He and Viren could have qualified for the world Mr Puniverse championships, but they could run the legs off everyone else.

Where you need muscular strength is in the upper leg muscles, because these control knee lift. You will develop that power, not by building strength as the weight-lifter or gymnast does but, more exactly, as the ballet dancer does. The muscles must be springy and bouncy over flexible ankles, so that you can maintain high knee lift, straighten the back leg, drive off the front of the back foot and whip that foot through for a long, fast stride. It will not come to you overnight; it might not happen at all; but the phased programme in this book will get you nearer that ideal than anything else tried anywhere.

The ankles play a bigger role in speed development than most people realise, which is why I include a phase specifically designed to give them strength and flexibility.

To understand what you are aiming for, picture how the ballet dancer stands tall. Flexible, powerful and seeming barely to touch the ground at all as he or she moves. America's greatest sprint coach, Bud Winter, emphasised running tall; the Australian middle and distance coach, Percy Cerutty, called it "lifting yourself out of your pelvis". You should feel as if you are centimetres taller than you are. Far too many runners do not get that feeling or attitude. They sit in a bucket as they run, if you can picture that alongside the ballet exponent.

I have dealt with the bucket-sitters by filming them in action, showing them the video and then setting them straight within a week, knees up, bounding along, completely in control and wondering how on earth they managed before. It needs only an understanding of the problem and confidence to tackle it to get you running correctly. It is a factor you should check constantly as you run. It might not come easily but it is what you must aim for. Any improvement will add to your speed and your enjoyment of running.

When you start using running muscles, expect soreness. It is a normal reaction and the remedy is not to stop until the pain goes away but to keep running, perhaps more easily. If you stop, you will go through the soreness phase again; keep running and the body's own defence mechanisms will attend to the problem. The soreness is the muscle's reaction to doing something it is not accustomed to, and possibly the tearing of muscle sheaths which have become gummed up through inactivity. Neither is life-threatening. A torn muscle, although it is unlikely if you use a sensible approach to the exercise of running, is another matter, which we discuss in a later chapter.

Just keep in mind, as you patiently work towards that goal of becoming a tireless runner, that only good things are happening to your body. The heart, the lungs, the muscular system and the circulatory system are all experiencing a revitalisation. Particularly, you will be building new capillary beds which will improve the distribution of blood through your body.

One counter to that stiffening and tightening that comes with age is more concentration on supplying and loosening calisthenics — up to fifteen minutes a day — because it helps to support muscles and tendons against injury.

Muscle balance is often neglected by coaches. Think of sportsmen who break down with popped hamstrings. The cause usually is that the quadriceps in the front of the thigh have been strengthened but the hamstrings behind the thigh have not, and when the athlete pulls his leg through fast the hamstring is torn. Cycling, because it works on both sets of muscles, and the stairs and uphill running exercises in my programme solve that problem. Weightlifting is an exercise that tends to build quads at the expense of the hams.

Triathletes do not have much trouble with injuries because their multiple disciplines balance all muscle groups perfectly.

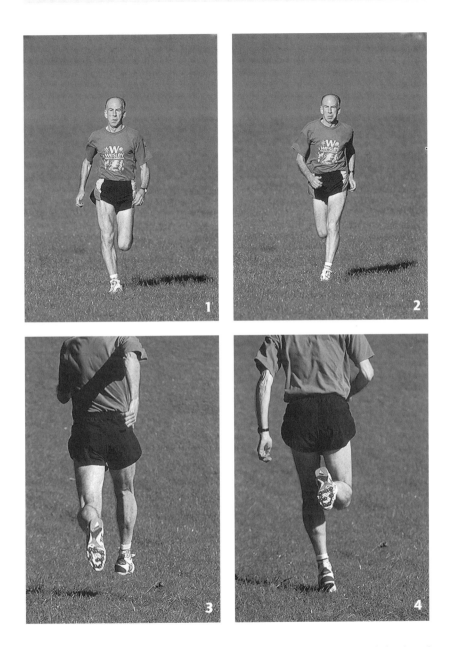

Running tall – fast relaxed running with good knee lift, high back heel and leg extension.

Fast, relaxed running. Note the back leg drive, perfect body angle and arm movements.

WHAT HAPPENS INSIDE   31

6 WHAT HAPPENS INSIDE

My system is all about making the human body more efficient in its uptake, transportation and use of oxygen and, therefore, more capable of improved physical and mental performance; more durable and enduring in whatever activity it is required to perform; and more likely to last longer in that condition. This is achieved by applying a steadily increasing level of work to push progressively the aerobic capacity of the body higher and higher.

Confining this exercise to an aerobic level is vital in the early conditioning stages because aerobic exercise makes efficient use of the oxygen supply from the lungs; anaerobic activity exhausts it. Under anaerobic conditions muscles will continue to contract for a length of time, but the restoration of an adequate oxygen supply soon becomes vital or the muscles cease to function. Whatever the exercise, it becomes impossible to continue it.

Drs Laurence Morehouse and Augustus Miller, in their book, *Physiology of Exercise*, explained that aerobic activity is sustainable because it makes efficient use of energy drawn from the oxygen supplied to the working muscles, but anaerobic activity is not sustainable because its use of the energy is inefficient.

The heart is just another muscle – but the most important in the body – which pumps oxygenated blood from the lungs through the bloodstream to the muscles and back again. My system teaches the heart to work progressively harder to shift more blood with more oxygen to where it is needed. Only one group of the multitude of muscles in the body can work long and hard enough to maintain a reasonably high aerobic pressure on the blood, vascular, and cardio-respiratory systems to achieve that desired result. They are the quadriceps, the large muscles at the front of the thighs.

The evaluation of various sporting activities has determined that this constant pressure is best achieved in cross-country skiing, which works all muscles but particularly the quadriceps. This is a sport confined to relatively few but, luckily, the activity which comes a close second to it is one that is available to just about everyone — running. Cycling, rowing and walking are next in line, but running scores higher than they do because the runner has to lift body weight against gravity, mainly by using the upper leg and thigh muscles. Cyclists and rowers sit down, walkers do not employ the high knee lift and leg drive that running, and merely jogging, requires. Swimming is another fine exercise but loses out on its developmental aspect because the swimmer's body weight is supported by the water it is moving through, and the required level of pressure on the heart is not exerted as it is in the runner.

It is inarguable that you cannot build a good house without first laying a solid foundation. Equally, you cannot establish good physical condition before you construct a sound aerobic platform. We can use many exercises to develop muscular efficiency and strength but the key to real fitness is muscular endurance.

A small girl marathon runner was tested against two beefy German shot-putters many years ago. These large men, briefly, could shift heavy weights a considerable distance but their blood vascular and cardio-respiratory systems were poor, and the girl, half their weight, had twice their cardiac output from a system that was 100 per cent better.

Particularly as we get older, we need to keep our muscles toned to maintain good muscular strength but, more importantly, we need to improve our cardio vascular system. Improve the blood flow from heart to lungs and back and we assimilate a much higher percentage of the oxygen we breathe in. And when we get extra oxygen into the body we can improve the circulatory system.

We already know from testing that older walkers, distance runners, cyclists and other athletes have well-defined and efficient circulatory systems many times more developed than those of sedentary people.

To consider the problem in a little more detail. The chemical which is our source of energy is adenosine triphosphate (ATP). The ATP stored in working muscles is sufficient to work for only a few seconds, but the muscles also contain creatine phosphate which rebuilds ATP, but only for about 15 to 20 seconds of strenuous exercise. This is where the fine balance between aerobic and anaerobic exercise plays its part. A marathon runner, employing a moderate work-rate, can get enough oxygen to burn fat and glycogen economically. This enables ATP to be rebuilt as fast as it is being used. The trained runner, working aerobically, can continue therefore for several hours or, in the case of ultra runners, for day after day of steady running.

But when the runner sprints or shifts his work-rate into the anaerobic phase, oxygen is no longer absorbed fast enough for the fat and glycogen breakdown. So the body cheats and does it without oxygen. The difference is that aerobic metabolism produces innocent wastes, water and carbon dioxide, but anaerobic metabolism produces lactic acid, which progressively clogs the muscles and interferes with their functioning.

In aerobic exercise one molecule of glycogen forms 38 molecules of ATP; anaerobic exercise yields only two, and that is the striking difference between the two and the compelling reason for learning to run aerobically. Morehouse & Miller calculated that severe anaerobic work is only 40 per cent as efficient as aerobic work.

The trained runner can get away with spasms of anaerobic action such as climbing a hill or kicking in a burst of speed to shake an opponent, and there is often some anaerobic reaction when you begin a run, until your aerobic mechanism gets the message, reacts and takes charge. Bear this in mind and guard against starting too fast in racing or training, or neglecting to warm up adequately.

The elite runner covers distances at high speeds because his or her muscles break down and release fat from the fat cells and oxidise the fat as fuel. The fat becomes the main fuel because, when muscles are mainly metabolising fat, the oxygen demand is greater than when burning glycogen, so the runner must either take in more air or slow down. So fat is not the preferred fuel for fast running for most people, hence the need to develop a system that staves off the need to demand it; but the trained marathoner burns fat efficiently, conserves glycogen and has that available for the fast finish over the final kilometers of the race. In races under 10 km, runners burn glycogen almost exclusively.

No matter how deeply you breathe, your muscles' use of oxygen is limited to your maximal aerobic capacity, which is known as VO2 . This is a complex calculation based on the amount of oxygen you can consume in a minute, divided by your fat-free weight, which indicates that, all other things being equal, the large athlete can use more oxygen than the smaller one. The VO2 varies considerably. A normally active male in his twenties can use between 44 and 47 mls of oxygen for each kilogram of his fat-free weight each minute; top endurance runners reach more than 70 ml/kg/min; women, because of their lesser muscle mass, generally score lower than men, but this gap in capability is closing as more and more women follow training schedules as tough as men's.

The marathon is a good indicator of the variation. The top runners will be running around three-minute kilometers aerobically on their high VO2. At the back of the field will be runners who could not run one kilometer at that speed without becoming totally anaerobic.

Another governing factor in athletic performance is your body's balance of red (fast twitch) and white (slow twitch) fibres. This balance cannot be changed, although the efficiency of both fibres can be improved by exercise, so it follows that the person with a higher percentage of red fibres can develop greater speeds than the person with a lower percentage. It is the difference between the sprinter and the distance runner. The slow-twitch fibres are best for aerobic metabolism, the powerful fast-twitch fibres for anaerobic metabolism.

The diaphragm and extensor muscles that maintain posture are mainly white low-twitch fibres, and the muscles in which the red fibres predominate, including most of the flexor muscles, are specialised for speed and tire more easily.

So, essentially, the aim is to develop oxygen uptake to make our body machinery more efficient with the hopeful end result that we will delay the aging process. Certainly we will improve muscular and mental endurance. When we do not tire physically, we do not tire mentally either.
I have already proved that high school boys and girls who improved athletically also became better students, able to study longer and more effectively with less mental fatigue. There was a distinct correlation;

several who became national athletic champions also took top academic prizes at their schools. In Finland I was publicly criticised for laying out training programmes for high school boys which were considered too severe and likely to upset their studies. Three of those boys won Finnish high school championships events and one of them became captain of his school.

The successful sportsman and the academic swot can be the same person. The same results have been achieved with men in their middle and late age who took up jogging for fitness and subsequently remarked on their ability to work longer, harder and more efficiently without becoming mentally exhausted.

Uphill drill – a bouncing action with high knee lift, good leg extension and slow forward momentum to work on thigh muscles.

Another view of Magee's relaxed fast-running technique. Lydiard described him as a "ballet dancer of the road", light and smooth on his feet and totally relaxed.

7 GETTING STARTED

For the raw newcomer to running I have two vital pieces of advice: one, discuss your intentions with your doctor and ask him to check that there are no medical conditions which might cause problems; two, **train do not strain**!

The Americans for decades have worked on the alternative principle that there can be **no gain without pain**, ignoring the reality that my system of conditioning and endurance training, without pain, has become the dominant system wherever successful athletes are found. The disturbing fact is that the United States, a country with a huge population and theoretically better-endowed than most to produce an abundance of talent, has consistently failed to become a significant force in middle and distance running.

Next, consider your equipment. It is minimal as far as clothing is concerned – light, loose-fitting and comfortable shorts and tops for summer running, warmer gear for colder months, and good shoes. The shoes are your costliest and most important purchases and they will be costliest in a physical way if you do not buy the right ones. I suggest you read the chapter on shoes in this book before you go near a sports shoe shop. The shop sales staff may be friendly and appear helpful but they are there to sell as many of their shoes as they can for the best prices they can get. They may tell you the most expensive shoes are the best but this is frequently not the case at all; many of the top-price brand-name shoes may look great and appear to have, like top-of-the-range motorcars, all the extras for better performance, but can only cause you strife.

Read, too, through the sections on foot care and injury prevention, and on the correct running style to get the most out of the exercise at the least cost and effort.

Your first run is critical in giving you an indication of your level of fitness or lack of it, so you must approach it carefully and sensibly. It is not a sprint and it must not involve speed running. Because it is vital that you do not overdo your initial exercising I will repeat the method: go out for five minutes then turn and go back, trying to maintain an even pace, however slow it may be.

If you take longer to get back you have learnt your first lesson – you went out too fast. This will teach you your own capabilities. Next time, go out slower so that you can come home in the same time. If there are other runners about, ignore them. Do not get into groups that force you, as a matter of pride, to try to run faster than you can at this stage.

You are likely to encounter many older runners who can leave you for dead over any distance. Take no notice. Instead, be patient, take the time I recommend to lay the first footings for your future foundation of stamina and it is possible that, unless they are following the same guidelines, you will be passing them in the not too distant future.

When you can comfortably run that five-out, five-back, begin adding time. When each longer run becomes comfortably easy, build on more time, always observing the long-short-long-short, hard-easy-hard-easy rule to give your body recovery time between the longer runs. It will need it.

As people age they tend to lose flexibility, and therefore their speed. It is important for them to consider this and work at exercises and running drills to reverse this trend. This is a combination of stretching and relaxed running on a regular basis, keeping any stretching exercises within individual limitations. Because you know someone of your age who can still touch his toes with straight legs, does not mean you should try to emulate him or her. We all have differing degrees of flexibility. Murray Halberg for example, was a brilliant middle-distance champion and superbly fit but he could never touch his toes. Nor could Bill Baillie, the Olympian and all-rounder who won New Zealand titles from the 800 metres to the marathon and is now a world class masters triathlete and and ironman competitor.

If you strain in your effort to improve flexibility, you risk pulling sinews away from their attachments to the bone. Just a little more flexibility is preferable to damaging yourself trying to regain the elasticity of lost youth.

Once you have laid your endurance foundation – the level at which you can comfortably and aerobically run for an hour, two hours or even more at your current pace – go to the track at least once a week and do fast relaxed running over 100 metres on the straight, as fast as you can, keeping any wind there might be behind you and thinking only one thing: running tall and relaxed. Jog on round the track until you are 50 metres from the straight then pick up speed gradually and go through the 100 metres drill again. Try this up to ten times depending on how you feel, and then cool down for about half an hour with easy jogging. After a time, believe me, your speed will improve significantly. Masters runners using this technique properly have become great speed runners.

If you plan to be a competitive runner, follow the schedules in this book for the distances you contemplate running only after you have achieved that necessary basis of stamina and endurance which has been the priority goal of all my athletes. Whether they have been 800 metres runners or marathoners, they have all laid the identical platform by following my marathon-type conditioning programme – an extended period of running up to 160 km a week, plus a similar distance of easier jogging. It seems a big mileage but many masters runners have been astonished by the ease with which they can attain that level of running. You may opt for lesser weekly conditioning mileages, but the pattern of long-short-long-short must be followed. Never put pace before patience.

The schedules are for guidance only. It is not necessary to adhere strictly to them because people differ in so many ways. Train how you feel within the schedule pattern and you will improve.

Just as the top competitive runner does, you have to train on hills regularly, and use the hill exercises because they improve speed and performance markedly. A little and often is the best approach. It is the same with the sprint training phase: work within your own limitations.

The pattern is important because it is designed to gain a balance in training and, in the end, bring you to a peak for the important runs you have chosen, whether they are fun runs, short races, half or full marathons. Because the same development is necessary for all events, the initial training is basically the same until the last six to ten weeks, when the training is co-ordinated for the specific distances being trained for.

And, throughout the training, the dominating mantra for success must be: **train do not strain**.

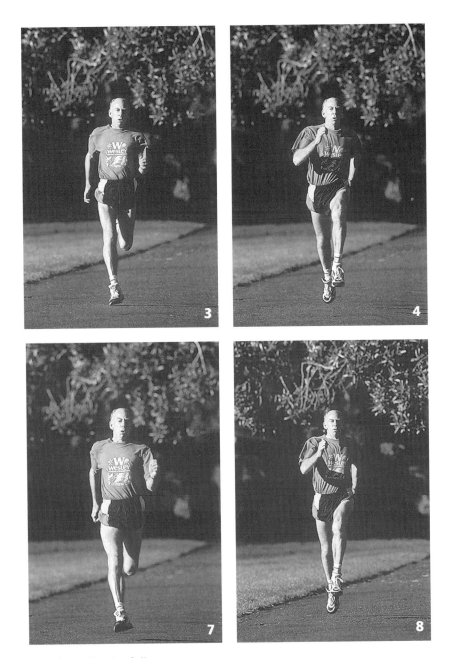

Running tall - the full sequence.

8 DO NOT MESS WITH YOUR SCHEDULE

If you are a beginner at the running game, do not try to shortcut the conditioning programme before you embark on a schedule. Give yourself as many months of preparatory running as you can, mostly at a strictly aerobic level with some once-a-week sprint sessions as referred to earlier to boost the process of becoming a faster, stronger, more enduring runner than you might have believed possible. Use Sunday, or whichever day is most convenient, for your long run of the week, aiming in time to be out there enjoying yourself for one, two or more hours; take it really easy a couple of days beforehand and, in the rest of the week, alternate long and short runs as you feel. The important thing is to give yourself recovery time between the longer runs. The preparatory work you put in during this period will stand you in good stead for anything you choose to do in the years to come.

Mix up easy running on hills and flat courses, vary your running routes as much as possible to avoid boredom, get into parks or onto golf courses if they are available, add in some fartlek-type days. Fartlek is, quite literally, fun-running; you mix bursts of speed, slow jogging, easy running, hills and hollows just as you feel like it.

SAMPLE WEEK SCHEDULE FOR BEGINNERS:

Monday:	1/2 hour jog
Tuesday:	1/2 hour fartlek
Wednesday:	1/2 hour jog
Thursday:	1/2 hour fartlek
Friday:	1/2 hour jog
Saturday:	1 hour jog
Sunday:	1/2 hour jog

In long runs: it is the speed that stops you; not the time of running. You can run too fast; but never too slowly to benefit.

After as many weeks or months of this conditioning as you can give it, you can begin to apply resistance in your running and at a faster pace. This phase is slightly anaerobic. It includes hill training, up and down hills, employing three different exercises – bounding, springing and running – in a co-ordinated routine, and some timed running over the hills as well. The objective is to use your body weight against gravity to develop more powerful, springlike muscles while the downhill sections build speed by allowing you to stride out fast. On flat areas you use some wind sprints to begin to improve your anaerobic capacity.

You need about four weeks of this to prepare you for the proper anaerobic training phase, when you will need to handle some solid workloads without feeling distressed. This period also lasts about four weeks and brings your anaerobic capacity to near its maximum potential. It involves three days a week of heavy load work, in which you can do any kind of anaerobic work you feel like, such as long distance runs hard over five or ten kilometres, or hard repetitions over whatever distances you choose, or hard runs on forest trails, or over undulating country, if either is available to you.

The repetitions can be run wherever you like. You do not need a track and you do not have to measure the distance or count the times you run over it, but for the best reactions the "reps" should be over at least 600 metres and you should run them until your body tells you it has had enough. Stop when it does.

This is my alternative to interval training, which is useless and even damaging because no one can possibly know exactly what any individual should do with times, distances or numbers. The stopwatch is your enemy when you try to do interval training. In conjunction with the "reps", you will need to work on your leg speed with typical sprint technique running and leg speed exercises.

In the final six weeks you concentrate on co-ordination work to accustom yourself to the speed and distances over which you intend to compete. The long "reps" are replaced by short ones and wind sprints to sharpen your whole body and its reactions. The short, sharp work enables you to hold your anaerobic capacity at the level you attained in the previous phases. This work is mixed with easy fartlek and you should do some development racing by entering underdistance or overdistance events on a weekly basis, adjusting each race according to your reactions in the previous one and the mood you are in.

It is important during these phases to maintain that balance of one day of hard work followed by one of easy work, and also to do some sessions of long, fast but relaxed stride-outs. Once a week you need a long, steady run for an hour to an hour and a half. All this may sound hard but, if you have prepared yourself properly, the various workouts will capitalise on that condition and build your speed even higher. This final phase should actually be more enjoyable because the work is comparatively light, the anaerobic sessions are short and sharp, and the long running is neither too fast nor too far.

You train to race – not keep on training hard

You are going into racing at this stage so, once more, the emphasis has to shift. Training is over and your purpose now is to keep yourself fresh and sharp for the races you intend to enter. You recover from hard racing by jogging the next day and doing some easy stride-outs the following day. If your race performance suggested you need more sharpening, you can add some wind sprints, but you must be thinking of conserving your energy for racing. As long as you have established a good background of conditioning, and take care to recover fully from each race, you can hold your form for a long time. If the conditioning has been skimped, that form is unlikely to be sustained.

If your competitive programme involves just one major race, such as a masters championship, but you want a season of semi-social or fun running, with five or ten kilometres gallops once a fortnight or so, you can mix your training, still keeping it balanced, and actually feel your improvement. This is achieved by using my race week/non-race week continuation schedule, which can be used for cross-country, road racing and even track racing. In the non-race week you push your training harder; in the race week you ease off. In the hard week you employ some anaerobic volume running, some fartlek, some long aerobic running and some technique or speed training, with a couple of timed, measured trial runs at less than full effort to assist your co-ordination. You still do the longish run. The race week is confined to short, sharp wind sprints, some easy fartlek, an underdistance trial, some stride-outs and some jogging, with the long, steady run shortened.

This programme is for masters who want to enjoy their running rather than aspire to be champions. It will enable them to race consistently at a personally satisfying level. It will not pay them to try to race ten kilometres every week, but they could easily manage that every fortnight or three weeks, with five kilometres races in between.

Half-marathoners can comfortably run an event once every month to six weeks, and it is possible to run a marathon every two months, provided full recovery is achieved after each race. Failure to do that will pull condition down and open the runner to injuries and a loss of form which may be impossible to regain without a return to another conditioning or retraining phase.

Full recovery cannot be rushed; apart from jogging easily and lightly, and maybe enjoying some brief fartlek sessions, the recovering marathon runner should do nothing but jog easily for a fortnight after a race.

It has been argued that distance runners should attempt no more than two marathon races a year but this is nonsense. It may be true of the elite runners, but the average masters runner could easily go out and run 42 km every week in training and, as long as he or she follows every marathon with full recovery and stays away from the temptation of "that ten or five kilometres fun run next week", could enjoy six marathons spread throughout a year.

New Zealander John Campbell, who returned to running after a long break, became for a time the best masters marathon runner in the world. He won several marathons around the world in very quick time, tended to get faster rather than show any loss of form, and made enough money to set himself up in business. He was New Zealand cross-country champion in his late 30s, and ran his marathons through his early 40s.

He and another outstanding New Zealand marathoner, Jack Foster, both demonstrated the perfect light-on-the-feet, high-knee, relaxed running style. Foster was 41 when he ran 2:12 for the distance and, at 50, missed beating 2:20 by a mere 24 seconds.

Lloyd Walker, at 41, was a good cross-country runner when he adopted my schedule. At 42 he finished in the first ten in the famous Honolulu marathon; at 43 he too clocked 2:16 in a marathon in Hamilton, New Zealand.

It is a significant factor that all these runners were also good cross-country runners. The two disciplines work ideally together because cross-country running teaches relaxation. It is essential when you are tackling country courses, often in muddy conditions, to learn to relax. You can always spot the ones who are relaxed because they run easily and upright, and there is no mud up their backs when they finish. The strugglers, who have to lean forward and lose the correct leg and knee action, fling oodles of it up their backs.

Another great example of masters running is Priscilla Welch. She began running when she was 35 and in her 40s took the New York marathon in 2:26, which is a fantastic time for women, and would be for most male marathoners.

Chicago`s Steven Goldberg was 37 years old when he began training to my beginner`s marathon scedule. Three years later, at 40, he beat the noted runner Hal Hidgen back into second place in the US masters` championship marathon. When I met Hal later, his defeat by Steve came up in our conversation and I mentioned that I had trained him. "No wonder," Hal said, "I couldn`t catch him."

Recently, I received a letter from a Lindsey Schroeder, of Hastings, New Zealand, reminding me of a talk we`d had in December, 1988, about the application of my conditioning system to the sport of power pulling. I used to be known as the tug-of-war. Lindsey said he`d adopted my conditioning theory and his team had accomplished a remarkable treble by winning New Zealand Power-pulling titles over three weight grades - 30years apart in 1969, 1970, and 1999.

The significant pointis that Lindsey is now 62 years old. His team of six have won six straight national titles and out pullled teams phisically imposing simply by their development of a high level stamina. They are veterans with a total of of 217 years of cumulative experience to add to their endurance training.

"To highlight the results of your methos, it gave us considerarable pleasure to have our heavier opponents sweating while we were only warmed up," Lindsey wrote. An accompanying newspaper article noted that, in training, he pulled more than 360kg in one 30-second long practice repitition.

Almost coincidentally, I have just received a letter from another Schroeder, Arthur, of Sidney, Australia, trying to find a copy of one of our very first books, *Run For Your Life,* which, he said was one of the three books which radically changed his life for the better. The others were *Use Your Head*, by Tony Buzan, and *The Memory Book*, by Lucas and Lorrayne.

"I bought *Run For Your Life* about 30 years ago at age 40 and I started jogging straight away," Arthur wrote. "I jogged for the next 15 years - three miles each day - and it`s the best thing I`ve ever done".

A perfect view of the correct low, relaxed arm action.

9 LOVE THOSE FEET

We tend to take our feet for granted. They hang about at the ends of our legs and we generally take little notice of them. But their care and attention are vital to the runner. When you begin running you will appreciate as never before the role the feet play as your body weight, suddenly moving faster, hits the ground harder. Ankle, knee and hip joints will also come to your notice, and what might happen to them is related closely to how you are looking after your feet.

One of the not entirely beneficial spin-offs from the world-wide boom in running and jogging was the emergence of huge companies, mostly American based, dedicated to supplying the runners with all the equipment and gear they need and quite a lot they do not. It all looks very smart and fashionable. New designs and concepts follow each other in quick succession as the companies vie for their share of the market.

Shoes are the prime example. They have advanced from the basic sandshoe type of footwear to a staggering range of brand-name shoes with soles as thick as hamburgers, a conglomeration of bits and pieces in a rainbow of colours, and an equally staggering stream of claims that they provide more traction, offer more anti-shock cushioning, have special inserts to counter pronation and/or supination and, if the claims are to be believed, will make you run faster.

But the reality is that the modern top-of-the-market running shoe, far from adding speed, could cause more damage than it does good. I have always had this concern that the more fancy stuff you place between the foot and the surface it is running on, the more the chances are that normal foot function will be upset, even hindered.

About a decade ago, Steven E. Robbins and Gerard J. Gouw, of the Human Performance Group in the Mechanical Engineering Department at Montreal's Concordia University, reviewed a considerable volume of research through the previous ten years to compare the shock levels experienced by runners in barefeet and in a variety of shoe platforms.

They found that when people who normally wore shoes ran in bare-feet they exhibited shock-moderating behaviour, which was not evident when they were wearing shoes. This measured up with other findings that people who were habitually bare-footed were not subject to chronic overloading when they were running.

It has also been noted by me, as well as others, that most people, when they run bare-footed, show no signs of pronation or supination but develop one or other of these problems when they wear running shoes. And it is a fact that, in the days of Murray Halberg, Peter Snell and company, before the advent of the shoe marketing boom, running footwear was little more than a thin sole between foot and ground – and they never suffered from foot or leg joint problems.

One of the 1985 research papers studied by Robbins and Gouw suggested that "modern running shoes are not superior and are sometimes worse than the unadapted bare foot in attenuating shock during running". Another study four years later, supporting the notion that more expensive athletic shoes from major manufacturers are particularly dangerous to use, found a significantly higher incidence of injuries in those using more expensive shoes and in those who stated they had a brand preference, with all major brands showing a similar incidence.

What the research said was that the excessive cushioning and the gimmicks employed in modern running shoes create false illusions of protection which trick the body into not making the shock-absorbing reactions normal when running in bare-feet and may lead the athlete to run with greater impact, increasing the shock effect and the risk of damage.

Another interesting piece of research in California more than two decades ago, when jogging was taking off, discovered 241 injuries in 100 middle-aged joggers, and a whole new range of injuries was classified affecting joggers' feet, heels, ankles, legs, knees, thighs and hips, each with its own set of potential malfunctions and breakdowns. It is not difficult to connect this with the findings on modern running shoes.

The point we are making is that, although you may pay hundreds of dollars for the very latest in hi-tech running shoes, there is no guarantee that you will avoid any of these injuries. In fact, you will probably be assuring yourself, as you pay over your money, that you WILL suffer from them in one form or another. The only guarantee that goes with these shoes is that the aggressive shoe companies which produce them will be comfortably rich.

The less we interfere with the natural movements of our feet, the better we are going to perform, so shoes have to be avoided which promise to cushion and control what fits inside them in accordance with what the designers think should happen. The ideal shoe would be one that is very flexible, provides little more than another layer of skin under the foot, and has no upper to speak of. It may be possible, but it has not been proved yet, that the older shoes were nearer to that reality than the multi-coloured, gel- and bubble-enhanced, massively-soled ones on the market now.

Orthotics are another modern problem. During my training camps, I was amazed by the number of runners who discussed running technique with me, and revealed they wore orthotics in their shoes. They all told me they needed them because they either pronated or supinated. I videotaped them running without shoes and showed them that, bare-footed, they did neither. The orthotics were for the shoes, not their feet. Invariably, none of the podiatrists and experts who had recommended the use of the inserts – to correct shoe faults – had suggested any exercises to strengthen the feet and ankles.

Some people of course genuinely need orthotics to correct some malformation, but they are not as numerous as we are led to suppose. In most cases, orthotics have been recommended as a quick fix for a problem which has nothing to do with any malformation, except in the shoe.

The strengthening exercises are simple. Balance on the balls of the feet on a stair tread, a step or a thickish book, and raise your heels up and down. Put a rope or cycle tube round the front of the foot and gradually pull upwards. Pick up objects with your toes. These routines all strengthen the muscles of the feet and cost nothing.

With strongly-muscled feet you should get full flexion in running but not in the fancy modern shoes. Almost every shoe made today is far too rigid in the arch and is often made even more rigid by the magical inserts developed with the stated intention of improving your performance. You might as well try to run efficiently with skis attached to your feet.

The foot must be allowed to flex naturally, and if the sole of the shoe does not flex how can the foot inside it hope to?

Another misleading factor is the often-stated view of shoe sellers that you should allow about a thumb's width of space between your toes and the front of the shoe to avoid losing your toenails. How you are expected to push off the front of your foot, as you should, when the toe of the shoe is flabby, is beyond me. You lose toenails when the shoe you are wearing has not been sprung properly. If the top line of the shoe around the upper part of the foot is too loose your foot will come out; if it is too tight it will pull on the Achilles' tendon.

The shoe should not be too curved fore and aft underneath, so that it resembles a canoe. When you put your foot in it, it will flatten and set up pressure at the toe — and that could cost you your toenails.

You do not need extra length in your shoes on the theory that your feet will swell when they get hot during running. There may be slight swelling sideways but your feet are definitely not going to grow longer.

Some shoes are made too straight, some too curved. The normal foot has some curvature but the test is whether the shoe fits properly under the foot when you stand. You should not need stabiliser bars and foot counters to hold your foot in the shoe. In fact, you would probably run just as well in a gumboot as you will in some of these expensive shoes.

You would certainly run better in bare feet as Zola Budd, Abebe Bikila and sub-four-minute miler Bruce Tulloh, among many other good runners, did without experiencing any plantar fascia problems, which are caused by overly-rigid shoes, or some of the other troubles experienced with such shoes. Tulloh even ran at full effort bare-footed on cinders. The foot, given its freedom, is tougher than you might think.

So great care is needed in buying shoes. If you can, talk to other runners about the shoes they wear, any problems they may have had with any particular brands, whether they can recommend a make that does not cause problems. Do not be influenced into thinking that the most expensive shoe costs more because it is the best. It almost certainly will not be.

It is an interesting point that top-line runners who are sponsored to promote a brand of running shoe do not normally run in those shoes. They have shoes made specially for them, with individual lasts designed for their own feet. And you will often find that, within a season or two, they are promoting altogether different brands. It all a matter of where the money is, not the quality of the shoes.

In my early days as a runner we wore canvas shoes with extra rubber glued to the soles. They were reasonably light, very flexible. We did not pronate or supinate, we did not suffer from plantas fascia. The only foot problem we might have encountered was a bit of skin loss from the rough canvas, and the skin soon toughened up.

Another promotional fallacy is that you need a protective shoe when you are training and a light shoe when you are racing. This is another sales gimmick. Consider this fact: when you are racing is when you hit the road hardest. You do not ease back when you hit a downhill section, you are almost certainly running harder than you would normally do in training, so you are pounding the pavement much more violently than usual, particularly if you are a big person.

You should train and race in the same shoes, and they should be more like slippers than the kind of shoes being advanced as training shoes. You need a light, flexible mid-sole, plenty of resilient cushioning underneath — and ordinary EVA is the best you can get — and you should be able to feel that your feet's flexibility is not being hindered.

So, when you are looking for shoes to run in, try everything available for lightness, for easy bend, upwards and downwards, at the arch in the middle of the shoe, for uncluttered uppers and the least number of stabilisers, counters and inserts. Try them all for shape on your feet; a straight-last shoe could cause pronation, if they trap the foot at the back; if they are too curved, they could cause supination. As for size, your toes should be close to the front of the shoe but you should not feel the shoe pull down on them when you walk. If the soles are too thick because of the inserts and wodges of rubber, be aware that they could lead to instability when you are running.

Walk about with the shoes on both feet and your eyes closed and concentrate on feeling whether there are any pressure points at all inside the shoes. The salesperson may assure you that the shoe will stretch and pick up the shape of your foot but that is not true. If there are pressure points, look for another shoe.

The salespeople say shoes should be broken in carefully, but you should be able to go out in a brand-new pair and run for an hour or two without marking or damaging your feet. A properly-made shoe does not need breaking in.

How you lace your shoes is important. They must be threaded so that, when the laces are tightened, they do not pull down on the sinews and metatarsals on the top of the foot. This restriction on the foot's freedom to move and flex properly can lead to problems.

Here is the correct way to do it: hold the shoe, toe away from you, and count the eyelets from the front to the back. Let us assume there are twelve. Number the left side ones 1, 3, 5, 7, 9 and 11; the right sides ones 2, ,4 6, 8, 10 and 12.

Put one lace end downwards through 1, the other end downwards through 2. Take the No 1 lace back and up through 5 and across and down through 6. Take the No 2 lace back and up through 4 and across and down through 3. Repeat this leapfrog to the back holes. This avoids the cross-over of laces between the top of the shoe and the tongue which occurs with the normal method, and which can set up the uncomfortable and potentially damaging pressure points. All the shoes you wear should be laced the way I recommend.

Watch shoe sole wear carefully. Excessive loss of the sole leads to stress right through the leg and hip and can also cause bone wear. Lost heel rubber should be replaced regularly, even as often as once a month if you are a high-mileage runner.

Uphill running, driving hard off the back foot, gives the quads a vital fall workout.

10 INJURIES

As we have mentioned, most injuries come from running shoes. If they influence the normal behaviour of your feet, the problems they create range from the feet themselves to the ankles, the knees and even the hips.

There are also problems from running on cambered roads, which causes the feet to roll to one side, especially if the shoes are not laced tightly. This can damage the miniscis and cartilage in the knees, an injury which may not be immediately apparent and could take years to develop. So it pays to think about the possibility and take precautions.

The bigger you are, the harder you will hit the ground, so the more risk exists for some damage. A suggestion for big people is that they confine their running to grass until they lose some weight, have developed the correct technique, and can run faster and, therefore, more lightly.

Chondramalacia is a common knee injury, felt just below the patella. Almost always the cause is the runner's failure to stretch his or her quadriceps before running. The quads are powerful muscles and, if they are tight when you begin running, they will not stretch as the knees bend and will pull the tendons which are anchored on soft bone under the knee.

Simply doing some squats stretches the quads. Or you can stand alongside a fence or wall, supporting yourself against it and swinging the inside leg backwards and forwards, alternating between a bent knee and a straight knee. Keep the exercise going for both legs until the upper leg muscles and sinews feel comfortably relaxed.

Hamstring pulls occur usually because the quads are too strong for the hamstrings. This is an imbalance in muscle development which should be corrected by hill or stair running, not fast but with a good knee lift. You should feel the resistance on the muscles you are trying to strengthen. This is not the bouncing action we advocate for ankle strength and flexibility but slow, positive upwards running.

Jogging or normal running are unlikely to damage hamstrings. They pop when you start sprinting – and they hurt.

Muscle tear is damage to the muscle sheath, different from a strain or sprain in that you can usually isolate the spot exactly. The muscle will not contract and the pain can be quite severe if the tear is significant. Use ice packs or cold water to stop internal bleeding as soon as possible. If blood escapes around the area of the tear, recovery will be much slower. Do not use massage for at least four days, and do not use the leg either.

Sprains happen quickly, usually when you slip, step into a hole or onto a stone while you are running. Swelling will be swift so, again, ice should be applied quickly and the area should be tightly bandaged. But, rather than put it up and rest it, use it. We have proved many times that a sprain will recover faster if it is used, and minor sprains or ankle wrenches, which may be initially painful, can be run right through without risk. In fact, if you stop, it will probably get worse. Keep running and by the end of the run you will probably have forgotten all about it.

But if the injury is something you cannot analyse properly, and does not show any sign of getting easier quickly, consult an expert and take the advice you are given to fix the problem.

Watch **blisters** which open up, even those so large you have to open them yourself. Bathe them with disinfectants and keep medication applied to prevent them becoming septic. They have a number of possible causes: the wrong kind of socks, if you wear them; foot movement inside the shoe; the wrong shoe size; or incorrect or loose lacing.

Another possibility is that you did not put the shoe on properly. When you put your foot in, jam the heel back as far as it will go and then lace the shoe firmly. Even the smallest gap between heel and shoe can cause friction and lead to the skin breaking.

After you have been running for a while, tightness may be experienced because the foot has swelled sideways. Then you can loosen the laces a bit. The swelling will never be longways.

Use olive oil, petroleum jelly or a similar lubricant, to avoid **chafing** in the crotch, across the chest or under the arms, which can cause enough skin damage to set up infections.

Stitch strikes mostly when you are running downhill. The diaphragm, bouncing up and down more than usual, extends the ligaments that hold the diaphragm to the skeleton beneath the rib cage. The solution is to condition firm but supple stomach muscles, which can be achieved by sessions of sit-ups but, unless you balance those contractions with back-bending, the muscles will become tight and inelastic and, when the heart and lungs expand, pressure will be exerted on the diaphragm.

A back-arching routine is good for muscle balance and suppling. One exercise is to lean forward with straight arms against a table edge or fence rail, the feet well back and then arch forward to bring the chest against the support. Hold and repeat a few times. You can get a similar benefit from simply arching back in the standing position, with your hands behind your hips, and holding that position for several seconds. Hip rotations are also useful.

Balanced muscles are also a safeguard against **back problems**, which affect runners who use forward-stretching exercises but neglect the inner muscles close to the spine. They have to be exercised the other way. The uphill running phase of my schedule is an excellent strengthener of those muscles. You can also lift light weights or concentrate on simple back-bending. You need to hold the position for a minute or so to get real benefit. Back-bending combined with sit-ups will, in time, produce very strong back muscles.

Cramp is caused by calcium deficiency. Muscle contractions and the central nervous system do not use a lot of calcium but, if you do not have enough for both during sustained exercise, it will be stolen from the skeleton, which will be weakened. The cramps attack when the lack of calcium stops the muscle contractions.

Calcium is absorbed best in a gluconate form, with vitamin D as a catalyst. It is particularly important before a marathon or triathlon.

Calcium lack can also cause **stress fractures** of the metatarsals and shins as they are continually under shock during running. This is particularly important for masters athletes, and especially women, who are also subject to osteoporosis. There is a belief that running with a calcium deficiency could encourage the onset of osteoporosis.

The stress fractures will hurt and will inhibit running. They do not show up immediately so you need to wait for ten days for an x-ray if you think you might have suffered a stress fracture. If it is an injury, you cannot fix it yourself; you need your doctor or physio to get you through this form of injury.

Rigid shoes, which cause the whole foot to clap down when the heel strikes the ground, particularly in steep downhill running, are one cause of **shin splints**, which is damage to tight front shin muscles.

It would appear that the membrane between the muscle and the bone ruptures and a nervous irritation is set up. Tight ankle muscles which prevent the proper flexing of the ankle, or tight muscles under the calf, could be other causes.

The poor circulation of blood in the shin area slows recovery from shin splints. Again, use ice and, if you want to run, stay on the flat and preferably on grass. You can run uphill but always walk down until you are fully recovered. Your physio can help.

The prevention of shin splints is better than the cure and the best prevention is flexible ankles. You have to work on them – raising up and down while standing with the balls of your feet on a step gives full extension to the muscles and sinews both in front of and behind the leg. When you are conditioned for it, hill bounding and springing work exceptionally well for ankle and foot flexibility.

The backs of some running shoes bite into the heel just below the Achilles' tendon. This can lead to **bursitis**, a gristly growth on the bone which can get large enough to begin to put pressure on the Achilles'. This is a problem more likely to affect people with straight up-and-down heels, rather than those with bulbous heels. Fortunately, most shoes these days, whatever their other faults, are made with a u-shaped cutaway at the back which keeps the pressure away from the critical area.

A large bursar will require surgery to remove it but a small one, if it stays small, is probably something you can live with. It is similar to the bunions women used to get through forcing their feet into shoes that, in the interests of fashion, were too small for them.

My remedy if you have a bunion is simple: cut a hole in the shoe to give the bunion its freedom, but make sure the edge of the hole is softened or it will cause friction.

Heel spurs, which are bone growths under or on the lower heel, are a problem. I developed one by jamming my heel down on some hard object and, to avoid the surgery my doctor advised, I cut a hole in the inner heel of the shoe to accommodate the spur, continued running, and had no trouble with it. I realised after some months – and after carving out the heel of another pair of shoes – that the spur had vanished.

But it can be a painful condition and you should seek medical advice if it proves to be bothersome.

Many sports produce a rash of **cartilage** and **miniscis** problems in the knees. Footballers, because of the quick twists and turns they are required to make at speed, are particularly prone.

It happens when the player's body and leg rotate quickly while the foot is firmly attached to the ground by its boot studs. The miniscis is the pad inside the knee and the cartilage wraps round the bones. The jarring and pounding of running can wear or damage both of them.

If you do suffer from pronation or supination of the ankles, problems could manifest themselves in the knee through cartilage damage or straining of the ligaments and muscles around the knee.

The surgical removal of damaged miniscis or cartilage does not spell the end of running. Barry Magee, bronze medalist in the 1960 Olympic Games marathon behind bare-footed Abebe Bikila, had his cartilages removed many years ago but is still running well in his sixties. He is the model for photographs in this book.

Entire knee replacements may slow a runner down for some time, but it will not prevent him remaining active once recovery from the surgery is complete.

You can wear elasticised bands to help weakened thighs, knees or ankles but make sure that what you buy does not grip on the skin and chafe it raw, or inhibit the flexibility of muscles and joints. You can get a type of surgical stocking which is supplied in rolls, its advantages being that you can cut off enough to make several thicknesses if you want to and it does not roll up or bunch behind your joints. This type of bandage is excellent if you are protecting a recovering injury, such as a hamstring, because you can run freely while wearing it.

11 BENEFIT, BENEFIT, BENEFIT

The theory that running will help you to live longer may be disputed but it will certainly help you to live better longer. Athletes who, in the 1940s and 1950s, were running 160 km a week in training to my schedules tend to confirm that opinion, because many of them are relatively unchanged physically and are still running extremely well in their fifties and sixties. Some of my original joggers from the 1960s, and they were not young men and women then, are still turning in remarkable times in their late sixties and seventy-pluses.

Running makes you aware of many of the deterrents to enjoyable later life, such as smoking, excess drinking, eating the wrong foods and lack of physical activity. If you eliminate those from your life pattern, it stands to reason that your chances of better years towards the end of your life will be greater. Whether you will have more of those years is, as I say, debatable but, again, it is logical to argue that a better lifestyle means less likelihood of physical defects and the prospect of living farther beyond your normal span.

There is ample evidence that the fitness achieved through running enhances mental attitudes, even from depression to confidence and from overstress to relaxation, with amazing efficiency. Running promotes a feel-good condition which reflects in a better approach to work and other demands. It improves sleep patterns, and it breaks down social barriers. Lawyers and judges jog in groups with plumbers and carpenters, college students and school teachers, and they all get along famously through a common, levelling interest in their own well-being.

Competitively, masters running pits peer groups, locally, nationally and internationally, in contests characterised by friendliness and social togetherness. The rivalry can be as intense as it is at younger levels but the spirit tends to be different because the prime objective of masters' gatherings is competing rather than winning at all costs.

As we train, our blood pressure tends to fall. Systolic pressure (the highest point at the height of the heart's contraction) and diastolic pressure (the

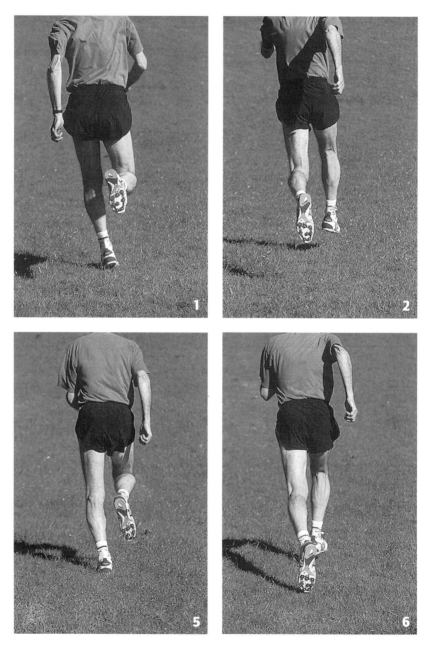

Bounding up hill. Long striding with hard drive off the back foot aided by

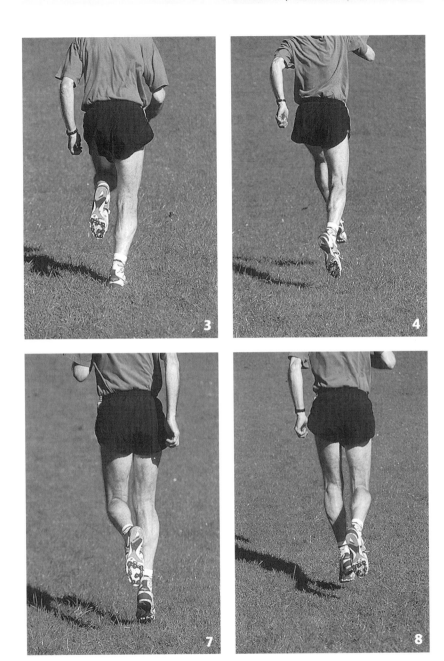

an exaggerated arm action.

lowest point, when the heart is relaxing) will improve because it is directly linked to an improved blood vascular system. This is why I encourage people with heart problems to become joggers, under supervision from experts in heart problems, with notable results.

A New Zealand pathologist told me the blood vascular system of a sedentary person could be developed twenty-fold by steady sustained exercise through the expansion and development of the body's huge network of arteries, arterioles, veins and capillary beds. I know that my endurance training methods dropped athletes' resting pulse rates down by twenty to twenty five beats a minute. Peter Snell reduced his rate from around 68 to 38. Now in his 50s, Snell is his age-group orienteering champion in the United States where he now lives.

Co-author Garth Gilmour's pulse slowed from a cigarette-accelerated 75-plus to around 50 when he took up running in his mid-thirties. At 73, although his exercising nows tends to be irregular, his resting pulse is still around 60, which proves another point: that a good level of fitness, once acquired, stays with you for a very long time.

High cholesterol levels used to be regarded as a danger sign but we have learnt since that cholesterols can be both good and bad and that some people, including myself, have naturally high levels which are not a threat at all. Everything depends on the type of cholesterol in your body.

Resistance to pain is governed largely by a pain-killing substance called endorphin, which is released from the brain's pituitary gland. Scientific evidence now suggests that exercise helps in encouraging that release and that it may have some physical part in the euphoria, or runner's high, reported by many ultra long-distance runners. It is also established that some people develop more endorphin than others, which gives them a greater tolerance to pain.

I believe a significant demonstration of this difference occurred in a race between two of my early pupils, Olympian Ray Puckett and Merv Hellier, both very fine athletes. They fought each other all the way in a 32 km cross-country race, thought to be the longest of its kind in the world, and

Puckett held a half-metre lead as they entered the last kilometre on a race course near Wellington, New Zealand. Hellier challenged all the way to the finish but Puckett still held that slim lead when he crossed the finishing line and immediately fell to the ground, completely out. Hellier, still running around, could not understand what had happened, but the fact was that Puckett, with his greater pain tolerance, had hurt himself to the absolute limit to keep Hellier behind him. Hellier could not do that, otherwise he might have been able to win.

Puckett's ability to squeeze out his last milligram of energy was similar to Roger Bannister's when he became the first runner to beat four minutes for the mile. He burst through the tape and stopped at once, unable even to stand on his own feet without being held up. He did it again in winning the Empire Games mile in Vancouver.

It is apparent that a lot of anaerobic training makes a major contribution to the release of endorphin but the comparison between two equally prepared athletes, one with a higher level of endorphin than the other, will not alter to any significant degree.

When we began the jogging revolution the great motivating factor at the time was awareness of the coronary problems that were affecting – and killing – a great many people, particularly in the business community. They were all working in heart attack country, they knew they should be doing something to protect themselves, they worried that they were doing nothing but they did not know what they could do in the way of physical exertion that would not perhaps trigger the very thing they feared.

Once they grasped the simple certainty that a controlled jogging programme did not impose the potential risks of, say, tennis or squash, because it did not stress unfit bodies, they were away. From then on the message changed. The jogging pioneers, most of whom had had heart problems, spread the message that, hey, jogging is fun, easy and good for you. And from there, of course, as all physical activities tend to do, jogging grew a competitive leg and masters' athletics was born. The sole purpose of jogging may have been personal individual fitness, but it is human nature to test yourself against your peers. Golfers do it, football players do it, tennis, squash players and ice skaters and skiers do it. Joggers now do it with astonishing ability, and many of them no longer feel comfortable with being described as joggers or even ex-joggers. They are athletes in their own right – and proud of it.

The fifteen minutes a day rule for jogging merely for fitness stays but those who have moved on from that still need the guidance of controls to help them achieve their full potential.

They need to evaluate their training on an almost daily basis, they must follow that routine of short run-long run or fast run-slow run, whatever their impulses might want them to do; they must recognise that cutting a training session short, or even skipping one if the mood of the day does not feel right, is not the end of the earth and will be more beneficial in the long-term than forcing the body into activities that, for whatever reason, it does not feel like doing at that time. It is a matter of listening to your body.

They must also recognise that extended breaks in the routine should be avoided – people with sufficient dedication find time to fit their work requirements and social lives around their running, rather than try to fit their running round their work and social demands.

They must realise that when they are into periods of heavy anaerobic training they must give themselves at least 48 hours, and longer if possible, for recovery. This is vital to prevent the central nervous and immune systems from breaking down. Piling more hard work into that vital recovery period will undo all the value of the training.

Motivation comes into play again when the weather turns sour. It is easy to look out at the driving rain or snow, or listen to the howling freezing wind and say, Oh, I will skip it today. But that is a cop-out. Properly clothed, properly warmed up, there is no danger in tackling the winter conditions – and there is a huge psychological boost in knowing you are out there, staying fit, while others are huddled inside, staying unfit. Many find bad weather running exhilarating and even look forward to its challenges.

In the same way, when we are in good physical condition, we can afford to indulge ourselves with occasional excesses. Chomp your way through a whole chocolate bar in the knowledge you are merely replacing the calories you burned up on your last run. Eat that delicious cake – and the cream inside it. Running actually heightens the desire for sweet things such as candies and cakes which might, in normal conditions, be bad for us, but running-fit people can yield to that desire, knowing they are not going to do themselves any harm.

The only limitation is that you do not "pig out" too often and you balance the occasional binge by regular attention to an increased calory intake through wholesome foods such as grain breads and starchy vegetables, and the natural sugar source of honey.

One prominent reason for running is to lose weight, and many are disappointed when the scales show little or no change. But loss of the weight of fat is often replaced by the weight of developed muscle, and some have known their weight actually to increase for that reason. Fat may be bulky but it floats and it is not the significant factor in weight that many think it is. Muscle, by comparison, is heavy so that a little muscle can replace a lot of fat.

The point is that you cannot burn off blood sugars until you become fit and fast enough to get into some form of anaerobic exercise. You will then burn off blood sugars 19 times faster than in aerobic exercise, and weight loss will begin to show.

The proportions of brown fat and white fat vary from individual to individual, but it is known that brown fat metabolises during sleep, so people with a high proportion of it can eat a lot and never get fat, while the person with a low brown fat content can almost get fatter just by thinking about food. Any marginal excess of calorific requirements will add weight.

So while it is misleading to claim basic jogging as a definite weight reducer, it does have a distinct role in adjusting the balance between fat and fitness. Since everyone is different from everyone else, there are no definite guidelines beyond the assurance that running, once basic fitness has been established, helps everyone.

The body fat content of top athletes is low; I believe John Walker's was measured at 3% when he became the first to crack 3:50 for the mile; and top marathoners are around 5%. Women naturally have more body fat than men and their marathoners are somewhere around 10%. So, with some exceptions, good distance runners tend to be thin and light. But we cannot all aspire to be like them, nor is it necessary to be like them to enjoy the pleasures of running and its associated feeling of well-being.

I have never been one to keep close control of my calorie intake, but it is probable we all tend to eat too much and that an occasional period of moderate fasting would be good for us. However, the regular athlete expends a lot of energy and is going to need more calories and will even need some of that fat we are encouraged to avoid. But go for polyunsaturated fats which are less likely to cause trouble than saturated fats.

The aim is to balance the intake of proteins and carbohydrates (carbohydrates play a major role in raising blood sugar levels) against the level of exercise you are doing. Your body is smart enough usually to let you know what it wants and what it does not want. As you do in running, listen to it in the kitchen.

As a supplement, I recommend honey. Easy to digest, high in calories, no bulk and it does not cause gas. Liquid glucose is another good substitute.

The best carbohydrates are in starchy foods, grains and so on but they have a tendency to cause flatulence, so the intake, particularly before competition, needs to be watched.

Lung capacity does not play a big role in athletic effort. Performance depends on blood flow per minute because that dictates how much oxygen you can gather in, no matter what your lung capacity might be. Exercise will not have much effect on your lungs; the benefit of proper exercise is in improved cardiovascular and cardio-respiratory efficiency.

People with problems such as sugar diabetes can still enjoy and get value from exercise, but my advice to everyone, especially those who have such handicaps, is to seek medical advice and guidance before you begin. This is an area we do not intend to interfere with.

How good can you be as a runner? Who knows until you try, until you push yourself towards your outer limits. Anthropomorphic measurements, muscle size and conformation, general metabolic efficiency and the ability to co-ordinate are all different and we cannot change that. But the slow runner can become a faster runner, and the fast runner can become an even faster runner because everyone can build endurance simply by improving their ability to assimilate, transport and use oxygen and then gain speed by systematically toning and improving their muscular system. Speed, power, reflexes and natural adaptability can all be influenced by sensible training.

So you do not have to be naturally good to succeed. You can be taught, or you can teach yourself to run with a better more effective style with an organism that is highly efficient, loaded with stamina and honed by systematic training to a fine edge. Relaxation plays a vital role in running; watch any slow-motion film of a good runner at speed and see how facial and other muscles flop around: that is relaxation.

We know today that women can do what was considered both impossible and unwise no more than three decades ago — they can train as hard as men. When one middle distance race was finally organised for women at an Olympic Games, the women finished in varying states of distress. Some fainted, others fell over. The reason was that none of them had trained for the event, so naturally they ran it badly.

Now, of course, the only thing they lack in comparison to men is muscular power. They can follow the same training schedules as men and run over all the distances that men do. In fact, they handle really long-distance running better than men; this was proved a few years ago in a 16,000 km race in New York when four of the first five finishers were women.

So, to sum up what we have discovered, jogging and masters running have proved that, at forty or seventy, we are no longer as old as we used to feel.

We know that we tend, as we get older, to show more endurance than younger athletes, as Carlos Lopez demonstrated when, at 36, he ran away with the Olympic marathon in Los Angeles. As mentioned earlier, many athletes in their late 30s or early 40s have run all over much younger rivals over all distances from 5,000 m outwards.

Your age when you take up running as a master is not particularly relevant. Obviously, if you have been active in your youth and have maintained a level of fitness it will be easier to become an efficient runner. But nothing need stop people of quite senior years, with little exercise or training background, getting out and learning to run and enjoy long distances or fun runs. A better cardiac system can be developed at any age. Hardened arteries need not be a handicap because other arteries which have never been developed can be brought into service through regular controlled exercise. In a sense you create your own bypass system. Many of the good masters runners did not begin until they were past forty years of age.

One of my first joggers, a man of seventy-plus, had had all the varicose veins stripped from his legs but the doctor who had done the stripping explained to me that the veins he removed were only ten per cent of the blood vessels in the legs. The others could not be seen, but the increased blood flow stimulated by running would develop them to replace those that had been removed.

12 VITAMINS, MINERALS, SUPPLEMENTS

Food likes and dislikes vary greatly and so do the diets of many of the world's great athletes. But they all perform well on what and how they eat, which makes it impossible to prescribe what is best for any one person. The medical profession and nutrition experts urge that a balanced diet is essential but, with the growing levels of processed foods and uncertainty about the origins of our fruit and vegetables, it is becoming increasingly impossible to say exactly what a balanced diet is.

Fruit and vegetables for instance, may be grown in soil from which some of the trace elements which contribute to that balance have been removed and to which artificial growth stimulators have been added. Can we be sure we get all the selenium, zinc, chrome and cobalt we need, and none of those additives we do not want? Our requirement may be small but each of these minerals is important for our metabolism.

So, while I have never been a fan for supplements, I have to concede that it is wise when you are involved in vigorous exercise to take multi-vitamins and mineral supplements. This does not mean you have to become pill-poppers swallowing mega doses of tablets but we need to consider, if we want to function efficiently, that we are getting enough from our normal food, whose quality and freshness can be affected by many factors. There are wide variations, for example, between the foods from the Arctic Circle, North Africa's tropics, and more moderate climatic zones.

So much has been written from so many viewpoints about diet analysis, mineral and vitamin values, carbohydrates, fatty acids, proteins and so on, that it is easy to be confused into seeking the answer by raiding the shelves of health food shops.

An example of the importance of trace elements: half a century ago the pumice lands of New Zealand's central North Island were brought into production. The developers poured in grass seed and artificial fertilisers and, when the grass was as high as a cow's belly, added the stock. The cattle immediately began to lose weight. Some died. Soil analysis showed the soil was deficient in just one trace element, cobalt, but it was enough to harm the cattle. Cobalt was added and the pumice lands are now some of the country's finest for stock raising.

Elsewhere in New Zealand soils are invariably lacking in zinc and selenium, compared with some parts of California, where some soils have too much of it.

Today's vegetables, which look so inviting in the supermarkets, are almost certain to come from market gardens' soil laden with growth-boosting artificial fertiliser but lacking in essential trace elements. This is a drastic change from the days when most New Zealanders grew their own vegetables organically in their back gardens. This swing to shop-bought vegetables is sure to be the same all around the world where Western lifestyles have been adopted.

The increasing use of colourings, additives and preservatives to processed foods is another danger, because excessive consumption of these is now recognised as fostering a highly toxic state in the human body, with the associated risks of cancerous and arthritic problems.

In fact some of the red dyes – used, for instance, to add the attraction of colour to ice blocks and other confectionary enjoyed by children, as well as adults – are known to be carcinogenic.

Gary and Steven Null, in their book, *Poisons in Your Body* (Prentice Hall Press, 1977), revealed that ninety per cent of the colourings used by food manufacturers were synthetic, and most were derived from coal-tar. Even Florida oranges were dyed. So were cat and dog foods, although the animals are colour blind. The colour was to attract their owners.

Interestingly, the Nulls found that the colourings were classified as "US certified artificial colour", which suggested they were certified for safety, when in truth the certification only meant that they met certain government standards which allowed the presence of an established percentage of impurities such as arsenic.

The Nulls' conclusions should also discourage you from ever eating another chicken in the US. To calm the chickens down while they are force-fed and fattened, they are fed tranquilisers to kill all the bacteria in the food they eat, including beneficial bacteria. Drugs, which include arsenic, and antibiotics are added to their mash – so you get to eat it too; to disguise the blandness of the pasty white flesh the chickens produce, they are coloured golden with artificial dyes; to add flavour, the enzyme hyaluronidase is injected; to cover the acrid scent the hyaluronidase gives off during cooking, a masking mixture of seasonings such as herbs and garlic is added.

Compare this with the diets of the stream of talented athletes coming out of the black African nations. They still live closer to nature than we do, they do not exhaust their soil by intensive cropping, grazing and artificially fertilising it, so most minerals and trace elements stay in the soil. Nor do they process their food as much as the western world.

Their food handling methods may not be considered hygienic by our standards, and the variety of their diets might not compare with ours, but they are enjoying much healthier, more nutritious diets than the rest of us, and developing a greater natural resistance to disease. Their simple but physical lifestyle is the main reason why they have become such dominant athletes.

The American magazine, *Women's Sports*, studied nutrition for four years and came to the conclusion that nearly everybody today needs vitamin supplements. You need them if you live in a smoggy city, if you train regularly in the heat, if you have an allergy, if you load on carbohydrates before a race, if you bruise easily, if you are about to compete.

The magazine added: "Life is action. There is nothing static about the body. What sparks and controls that action – the beating of your heart, the steady fire of your digestion, your breathing, your moving – are enzymes. Without vitamins, enzymes wouldn't work and neither would you. Without thiamine (vitamin B), the brain and nervous system collapse. Arms and legs lose their co-ordination. The eye muscles freeze into paralysis. The mind blackens into amnesia and coma. The heart stretches, swells – and stops."

Scary but true. So let us look at the role of vitamins in athletic performance.

Vitamin A, necessary for cell replacement, is the one vitamin people get too little of and it is also the one on which you can overdose, although only by taking mega amounts daily. Prime sources are fresh fruit and vegetables, worst sources are fast foods in general. "A" keeps the skin smooth, the vision sharp, the immune system strong and helps anti-stress mechanisms.

Carrots, sweet potatoes, spinach, apricots, and canteloupe contain betacarotene which, when·it is not killed by overcooking, converts to vitamin A in the body. More than 16,000 IU of "A" are in a cupful of cooked carrots. But the most concentrated source is fish liver oil and the best source of this oil is in vitamin A supplements. You can take up to 30,000 IU a day and if you also take vitamin E, the body's ability to absorb and use vitamin A increases sixfold.

B complex calms the nerves and works against depression, irritability, lack of concentration, insomnia, forgetfulness, anxiety and paranoia. **B1** *(thiamine)* helps to convert carbohydrates into glucose, which fuels the brain and the muscles. Prerace carbo-loaders should take 5 milligrams a day to turn the pasta into energy. Leafy greens, whole grains, nuts and seeds are thiamine-rich. **B2** *(riboflavin)* helps the digestion of fats and is found in broccoli and asparagus, milk and cheese, almonds and liver. Of the grains, wild rice is best.

B3 *(niacin)* causes a multitude of reactions in the body but the most important involves the red blood cells, which carry oxygen around the body. The last stage of the journey is through the hair-thin capillaries, which connect to the tissues. Each red cell is kept from other red cells by a negative electrical charge and niacin keeps them charged, which keeps the body charged with oxygen.

B12 *(cobalamin)* livens up the central nervous system, which communicates between brain and body. Liver is the best source but any animal product should do, except those American chickens.

Folate, from green, leafy vegetables, particularly cabbage, wholewheat, brewer's yeast, oranges, beet, beans, meat and eggs, helps gene formation, the body blueprint, including the oxygen-carrying red blood cells.

Pantothenic acid, needed if you train, compete or play in the cold, is found in all foods, except canned and frozen foods and anything made with white flour, which may lose up to three-quarters of its pantothenic acid.

Choline and **inositol** are two B vitamins in **lecithin**, a substance which is part of plant and animal cell walls. They enable cells to absorb fat, which, as a nutrient, is as vital as protein or carbohydrate.

Powerful **vitamin C** detoxifies heroin, nicotine, alcohol and cancer-causing pullutants, and a gram an hour will cure the common cold. It is a natural antihistamine. Increasing "C" intake a few days before an event in hot weather will beat the heat and sharpen your competitive edge. Found in fresh oranges and other citrus fruits and in potatoes, green peppers, parsley and broccoli. Frozen or bottled juices and potato chips have been stripped of most of their vitamin C.

The white inner skin of citrus fruits and the white column inside a green pepper are rich with vitamin C's close relative, **bioflavinoids**, which, have value in strengthening capillaries.

Vitamin E absorbs calcium and that is about all it does but, since calcium regulates muscle contractions, your heart could not beat without it. Not much comes from food. The source is sunlight so, unless you spend all your time indoors or completely cover yourself when you are outside, you face little chance of lacking in "E". It also has some effect in improving glycogen storage, providing more fuel for endurance sports, and protects cells from oxidation.

Processed foods are almost devoid of vitamin E — ninety-eight per cent is gone from cornflakes — whole wheat bread contains seven times more than white bread and brown rice six times more than white.

Our bodies carry about 1.3 kg of **calcium**, more than any other mineral, and most is in the bones and teeth. But if we took the remaining tenth of one per cent from our circulatory systems, our muscles would cease to contract. The vital amount of calcium is so exactly controlled by our systems that, if the amount falls a microgram or two too low, calcium is immediately taken from the bones to recover the deficit. Calcium also affects nerves and muscles, and extra intake will unknot muscle cramps.

Lack of calcium is the cause of osteoporosis, which strikes millions of the elderly, particularly women, so it should probably be taken as a supplement from the mid-twenties on, when bone loss begins. It has been suggested that a person who began calcium supplementation that early would, at the age of 70, still have the bone mass of a 40-year-old.

Calcium reduces stress fracture risk in athletes. Best sources are bone meal, cottage cheese, Swiss cheese, yoghurt, sardines and salmon, colard and turnip greens and tofu, but another excellent source is dolomite because this limestone product contains exactly the balance of calcium and **magnesium** that nature requires.

Magnesium is a natural tranquiliser, calms jumpy nerves and muscles and aids good sleep free from tossing and turning. It is also needed for the digestion of protein, fat and carbohydrate. After dolomite, good sources are whole grains, soybeans, nuts, leafy green vegetables, fruit and blackstrap molasses.

Athletes who do not sweat do not need extra **potassium**, but those who do and take salt tablets, which I advise against anyway, need double doses. People lacking potassium are more liable to heat stroke, and it should be noted that salt tablets force potassium out of the body.

Your daily **sodium** requirement is about 2,000 mg a day, but your typical salt-shaker habit delivers between 10,000 and 12,000 mg, far too much. Fill the salt shaker with natural spices and opt for natural unprocessed foods which provide a natural amount of sodium — and taste better.

Iron appears in a lot of foods as a fortifier, but the body readily accepts iron only from vitamin C and, anyway, other additives and preservatives block absorption into the body. One thousand mg with a meal will boost iron absorption tenfold.

Meat contains iron and helps iron absorption from other foods as well. Tea's tannic acid and regular use of aspirin are known to shift iron out of the body, which is one reason why iron is our most common nutritional deficiency.

But use it sparingly as a supplement because it is possible to overdose. The Vitamin C should be enough with perhaps no more than 20 mg of an iron supplement.

Chromium helps the body to use insulin, the hormonoe that regulates blood sugar. At the rate we eat sugar – an estimated 54 kg each every year – a lot of insulin is needed to burn it and that is where chromium helps. Two tablespoonsful of brewer's yeast a day supplies the need.

Zinc is involved in just about everything that happens in the human body. It is essential for sexual maturation, speeds healing, blocks the absorption of lead and protects against cadmium. Oysters contain 100 times more zinc than any other food but depend on red meat, liver, wheat germ and nuts. If you do not have oysters every day – and who does? – a 20 mg supplement a day does the job.

Certain areas in the United States are heart trouble zones, with more strokes per capita than anywhere else, because their soils contain less **selenium**, generally recognised as a cancer preventive and stroke stopper. It is in seafoods, whole grains, organ meats and brewer's yeast, beans, peas, spinach, bran, brussels sprouts and blueberries.

13 TRAINING SUMMARY

Let's recap a few of the angles on running which continually crop up in conversations. They may appear simple but they're areas where a lot of runners, especially people coming to it later in life, get confused.

When should you start training?

The sooner you start the better, provided you are a healthy individual and are not suffering from any injury or ailment. Inactivity does not improve the condition of the body. The body's fitness does not stay at a given level but either improves or deteriorates. If you do not exercise, you will not be as fit tomorrow as you are today. If you do exercise, you can skip the occasional days and you will stay as fit tomorrow as you are today.

Can training harm you, either early or later on?

Provided you train within your own fitness level to the pleasantly tired state - in other words, aerobically - your condition will invariably continue to improve, with your metabolism generally functioning better. Extreme use of anaerobic or excessive speed training can be detrimental to your health, as the continued low blood pH can upset the functions of some metabolic actions in your body. If you maintain a good ratio of aerobic exercise in your overall weekly schedule, you will continue to gain in general cardiac efficiency. Aerobic exercise cannot adversely affect a healthy heart. To the contrary, it will make it bigger, stronger and generally more efficient.

How often should you train?

The more regularly you train the better. Dr Hartialia, of Finland, once said: "The day that you do not train will take you two more days' training to get you back to where you were." This may not be exactly true but it is close to being right. You should exercise daily, even if it is only a short jog of ten or fifteen minutes, rather than doing tiring workouts with days of rest in between. For an athlete, every day's training is important for maintaining and advancing a fitness level.

With youngsters, there are psychological aspects to consider, since most don't want to be involved with only one sport or recreation. So, if you, as a master, are advising the young, it's not exactly a question of "Do as I do" but "Do as I say" and encourage them to play at training and take rest days if they really want to. Invariably, if they are given a schedule, they will be conscientious enough to try to keep to it but it should never become a task that takes away the pleasure.

Should you train more than once a day?

If time allows, it is advisable to train two or three times a day, provided there is no imbalance between aerobic and anaerobic efforts. Once the necessary anaerobic session has been completed - if there is one in the phase of the schedule you are working on - any supplementary easy or aerobic training will further improve you. This helps develop general cardiac efficiency and assist in the recovery from the low blood pH that may have developed during anaerobic training. By stimulating blood circulation gently or aerobically, you will assist your metabolism to improve.

Other aspects including the energy expended at work, must also be considered. However, even when you're physically or mentally tired, an easy jog in the park can work wonders in assisting your recovery and regaining you feeling of well-being.

But, and this is an important but, if the schedule says you are to run, say, 10 km on a given day, don't break that into two runs of 5 km each. What the schedule says is what you do and any other sessions are extra to that. Remember, if you cheat, the only person who suffers is you.

How long in time or distance should you run?

This is an individual consideration, governed not by age, but more by physical fitness. Quite young runners can go for up to two hours or more without resting. It is usually best to try to run for a given time rather than a given distance, so you avoid putting pressure on yourself to complete a course or finishing in a state of fatigue.

By running for a given time, you will not try to see how far you can go; you'll be governed by your feelings as you run and will quite often hold back in the early stages to make sure you finish the time comfortably.

It is advisable to run daily for a time that you can manage well. Then occasionally - say, twice a week - add another 15 or 30 minutes. This way you will gradually build up your endurance without getting into a fatigued state before completing a course. You will also avoid biting off more than you can chew in any training session. It is the speed that will stop you, not the distance to be run. If you go slow enough, you'll be able to complete progressively longer runs with ease. So, go for distance, not speed.

Where should you train?

Changes of scenery and different environments can stimulate you to train more consistently and better, so it pays to alter your training venues and courses from time to time. All sorts of terrain should be used often, with concentration on the type of terrain you will run over in a particular season. For instance, during the cross-country season, most of the work should be in and on the country.

But, when you're training for the track, it is often advisable to do all the training possible away from the track such as repetitions, sprint training of some types, and technique training. It can freshen your approach to training and make you more interested in the training you have to do on the track, such as trials and training work that require timing. The new synthetic tracks can cause tired or sore legs if they are used too often, because of the rebound that occurs when you are running fast.

For conditioning training to increase oxygen uptake, it is better to choose terrain that offers good traction, so you can run at a high aerobic effort without tiring your leg muscles too quickly. This is why roads are often best for high-volume aerobic running. Soft, rough or sandy ground tires the muscles, slowing you and reducing the circulatory system's pressure.

How much anaerobic training should you do?

An anaerobic training session should stop when you are tired enough from the oxygen debt incurred. Coaches cannot define this limit beforehand and can only offer advice about what workload is reasonable. You, the runner, must decide the stopping point, whether your training includes repetitions, interval work or fartlek.

In what weather conditions is it inadvisable to train?

You can train in extremes of temperature from minus-30 degF to 105 degF or even higher. However, if the temperature is low, it is important that the humidity is also low; otherwise your lungs can ice up. In Finland, where I coached in the mid-sixties, the humidity was usually about 20 per cent or less during very low temperatures, so we could run comfortably for two hours.

If the temperature is very high, you need a reasonably high humidity level too, so that your skin will stay wet with perspiration and help to cool your blood. If the humidity is low, you can dehydrate quite quickly and be forced to stop training. Remember: High temperature needs high humidity; low temperature needs low humidity. In other combinations, training becomes difficult, impossible or even dangerous.

Watch the wind in low temperatures; it can blister unprotected skin. If you train in cold climates, you need good protective clothing. Some runners suffer from hyperventilation because the muscles of the lower rib-cage controlling breathing become too cold to operate properly. Aprons of flannel or wool can be used to keep these muscles warm.

For heavy rain, it is wise to have good waterproof covering to keep out the worst of the rain and maintain reasonable warmth. If your legs are inclined to get cold, protect them by rubbing them all over with olive oil. It helps to maintain warmth and improves circulation.

Back in 1960, the coach of Herb Elliott, the late Percy Cerutty, was lecturing in new Zealand and remarked that only four runners had then broken 28 minutes for six miles. Two of them were Australians and none was a New Zealander, he said. His air of scorn angered me because I knew Murray Halberg could do it. He was off training then but I talked to him and he agreed to do it.

Three nights later, he ran his six. The night was cold and wet and the grass track was wet and soft but Murray had a hot bath and smothered himself in a liberal layer of olive oil. We then wrapped him up well and took him to the track. He turned on what I believe was an unequalled grass track performance, the world's second fastest six-mile (27:52.2) and the third-fastest 10,000 metres (28:48), and I know the olive oil had a significant bearing on the way he handled the poor conditions.

How long should you rest between seasons?

It is wise to keep training when one competitive season ends, rather than stop altogether. The training need not be too exacting. Light jogging for at least 15 minutes a day will help you to maintain your general condition and make it easier once you begin schedule training again. Your performance level in the next competitive season is governed by your aerobic capacity, so the more training you can do to improve this the better.

So, in the period between the end of the cross-country or track season and the beginning of the anaerobic training for the next competitive season, get in all the mileage possible. Two weeks of light jogging can help to freshen you up mentally and physically and will maintain and probably improve your general condition.

How many days a week should you rest and not train?

Mature athletes should train every day but some of the days can be rather light. If you train only six days a week, you can't hope to beat athletes who train every day. Anyone who loses 52 days' training a year isn't going to have optimum results. But, as explained earlier, don't force yourself out there if your body isn't really up to it for some reason.

How many days should you rest before competition?

If the competitions are important ones, then it is best to find out through trial and error what periods of rest or easing up suit you. Some athletes run better if they train lightly during the last ten days and do nothing for the two days immediately before the competition. Others find it better to keep going, jogging or even running through some fast stride-outs on the morning of the race. Whatever you do, realise that training hard during the last days before competition can only make your performance worse. But jogging lightly will usually keep your bowels in good order and help your metabolism because of the stimulation of aerobic exercise on the circulation.

What total amount of anaerobic training should be used?

The maximum anaerobic capacity of the runner needs to be developed for optimal results. This involves the capacity to incur an oxygen debt of 15 to 18 litres. I have shown that it is possible to develop this capacity in individuals with four weeks of intensive anaerobic training sessions every other day, with the other days used for recovery training. Before this, some anaerobic running is used for about four weeks, in the form of 50-metre sprints extending up to 200 metres in series of threes or fours, three or four times a day, three times a week. This is to cover the transition period from the slower aerobic training to the intensive anaerobic work.

The East Germans worked on a period of five weeks but my system of three intensive days a week for four weeks gets you closest to developing your anaerobic capacity to the maximum. Without the assistance of physiologists, you can usually tell by your feelings whether you are getting exhausted by the training. If you are, ease up on fast volume anaerobic training and use short, fast wind sprints over 50 or 100 metres, plus racing and easy fartlek sessions. You should be able to maintain that comfortably.

This is an important part of the training to control and it is difficult to estimate the volume and intensity of work that is most successful, because every individual's reactions are different. Go by your own awareness of your reactions – listen to your body – and adjust your training to suit.

But remember that a hard anaerobic session must be followed by a recovery period before another anaerobic session to avoid depressing the blood pH and preventing its recovery.

Should you be timed in training?

It pays to time some, but not all, of your training. To develop good pace judgment, times should be called to you or a whistle blown every 100, 200 and 400 metres until you develop an ability to judge pace accurately. With practice, you can develop this to a very marked degree.

On the other hand, I believe too much use of the watch during training can be detrimental because, on some days, it places too much pressure on the runner to maintain exacting effort. This applies particularly to anaerobic repetition and interval training, phases that many give too much emphasis. If you work to efforts that you feel happy about, you'll gain the desired results. For time trials and even-paced running exercises, it pays to use your watch. It's all a question of what training you're doing and how much control you need. Just don't become a prisoner of or a slave to the stopwatch.

Before Richard Tayler startled the running world by winning the 10,000 metres at the 1974 Commonwealth Games in New Zealand, he and I were working out at a local school. The school coach and his athletes wanted to know what times he was running his 400-metre repetitions in and how many he was going to run.

I said, "He doesn't know and I don't know. It wouldn't even matter if they weren't over 400 metres. As long as he's pleasantly tired when he's finished - and he won't stop until he is tired - he's going to get the physiological reactions I want."

No coach in the world can say exactly what an athlete should do as far as repetition times, distances, intervals and numbers are concerned. Nor can a physiologist. What is important to you, as an athlete, is that you know what you are trying to achieve and you go out and work at it until you do, I believe masters athletes, because of their experience and maturity in life, should have no problem with that do-it-yourself-your-way approach.

What is the use of running time trials?

The words time trials perhaps give the wrong impression of their use. Basically, they are used to develop coordination in running races over certain distances and to find any weaknesses and use the appropriate training to strengthen those weaknesses. Time trials should not be run at full effort but with strong, even effort, leaving you at the end with some reserves.

Don't place too much emphasis on the time resulting from time trials. The effects of any irregularities in your running are the important factors. Analyse lap times to discover if there are any variances in your pace at any particular stages of the trial. The danger, if you get too concerned about the elapsed time, is that you can lose confidence in your potential. Remember that when you are doing time trials, you are still training hard, so good times cannot always be expected. You cannot train hard and perform well at the same time.

Is there a difference between physical fitness and biological fitness?

Yes and I'll pass this over to Dr J C Fitzherbert, of Wollongong, Australia, who many years ago treated the fine distance runner Dave Power when he was hospitalised for problems apparently connected to the tremendous exertion he had submitted himself to in training and racing. Dr Fitzherbert said it was possible to draw a distinction between the two forms of fitness. Ideally, they should go together and usually they did; but there were circumstances in which biological unfitness from severe physical could result in structural changes.

"There seems no doubt," he wrote, "that little attention is paid, by high-performance athletes, to some of the important effects of loss of the essential trace minerals. It has been established that high-performance athletes, as well as losing salt, lose large amounts of zinc and magnesium. The loss of these trace elements results in very subtle changes in body physiology and biochemistry. Their loss can be exacerbated by the diets of athletes, particularly when it is a diet high in protein, which leads to greater requirements for the essential trace elements.

"Replacement of the essential trace minerals is made even more difficult because of the deficiency of many of them in the soil and hence in the food which athletes eat. Apart from the prevention of changes in physiology and biochemistry, their deficiency can lead to some loss of tensile strength, over the years, of collagen tissue, which is the basis for the not infrequent breakdown of athletes, sometimes when they are reaching the peak of their physical performance.

"The amount of zinc which is lost by high-performance athletes during training and competition cannot be replaced in their diet and their requirements could possibly be double or treble normal requirements."

This should be enough to send you back to the chapter on minerals and vitamins for a second and more thoughtful study of just what the human body needs when it is under the pressure of a consistent training regime.

14 RACING TACTICS

Go out with just about any bunch of joggers or fun runners and the first thing you are likely to sense is the element of competition among them. Ideally, they should all be content to run at the pace of the slowest, so that everyone benefits and nobody gets over-stressed but human nature always intrudes. This competitive instinct emerges as a desire either to seek your own potential or to match yourself against your peers to see who is the better.

Nothing wrong with that. It is why the masters movement has entered into so many sporting activities all around the world.

Another aspect of the competition amongst joggers is the inevitable use of amiable cunning and tactics to fox and outdo your rivals so let's have a look at the tactical side of masters' racing.

Middle and long-distance running is governed by several elements, all of which can be considered tactical. These include the athlete's basic abilities and development; the basic speed or the ability to sprint; endurance; the ability to maintain a fast, steady pace; the ability to vary speed in a race; the ability to use the most suitable distance for a finishing kick; the ability to exercise control, during a race, over yourself and over others; a consideration of opposing runners' abilities; the ability to see and assess the strengths and weaknesses of the opposition; the ability to recognise your own strengths and weaknesses; the ability to relate your strengths and weaknesses to the opposition's strengths and weaknesses; the ability to judge pace.

You must always be realistic and understand your limitations in running various distances. Among the principles I've just set down, basic speed is particularly important. Some runners are at a disadvantage because they don't have good basic speed and must force the pace in most races to try to take the sting from their rivals. They fear the final fast kicks and must work hard to take that kick out of the calculations. Often, this is achieved but there are exceptions. For example, in a strong wind, fast runners can sit in on the runner forcing the pace, letting the wind take its toll, and setting up a situation for a sprint finish when the front-runner is tired out. In such a situation, it is unwise to try to force the pace all the way; it is better to wind up, say, 500 metres from the finish, which might be far enough to test the opposition's stamina and weaken them for the final sprint. The fine balance here is that you don't run out of energy yourself. Try yourself out over various distances to determine the most suitable distances from the finish from which you can launch your finishing run.

Some runners can pick up speed quickly, others build to sprinting speed gradually. If you can kick fast, it is all right to be near the front when you do kick. If you can't, you would be wise to stay back a few metres, giving yourself distance in which to gather speed before passing the leaders. If you don't, you'll take them with you because you'll have lost the element of surprise. In situations like this, you really need to know your opposition, particularly who the fast kickers are who could cover your slow build up and then kick away from you. Trial and error methods will show you your most suitable kicking distance.

Runners with questionable stamina have been known to take the lead to try to slow the pace gradually. This works sometimes but, usually, other runners soon realise what is happening and bury the slow leader. What happens then is that he or she tries again to get out in front and subtly apply the brakes which leads to a series of sprints and surges. The one who will suffer most in this situation is the runner lacking stamina and trying to control the race pace.

The best ploy for this type of runner is to maintain an inside line on track or road, covering as little ground as possible, getting as much drafting assistance as possible and hoping the speed won't be too fast. Trailing the front runner is more likely to control the pace than front-running. Front runners often have doubts flitting through their minds — can I maintain the speed, how good is this runner sitting almost on my shoulder, should I back off for a while — and these doubts build up nervous tensions that can tie the runner up. When the dreaded — and by now expected — challenge comes, front-runners often lack an immediate and positive reply and let the rest of the field go by.

Very few important international races are won from the front, except by athletes so aware of their superiority that they fear nothing and no one.

If the speed is reasonable, stay back and avoid making your run too soon. Few athletes can master two sprints of more than 100 metres in the same race. So conserve your energy, both mentally and physically, for that one concerted final burst when you can afford to hold nothing back.

Tactics have changed through the years as more and more runners build their endurance to levels that were once the domain of only a few. For example, the great Russian Kuts used to spread-eagle his rivals by throwing in a series of 50-metres wind sprints during a 5000-metre race which they couldn't match. Today, that tactic might shake off some but the majority would probably absorb those sprints as well as the runner applying them.

The tactics of good running begin when the starter's gun goes off, because this is where pace judgment and self control are vital. Too often, runners go off to fast for their ability, simply because someone else has done so and they are foolish enough to follow, forgetting that races are won at the other end, not at the beginning. Too early, they are into oxygen debt and paying the price.

Nowhere does this mistake occur more often than in mass-start marathons. The elite runners get away first and settle into a rhythm; the rest spend minutes shuffling along the road before the field opens enough for them to begin striding out. Then, aware that the beginning has been little more than a walk for perhaps the best of a kilometre, they try to make up for lost time, setting a pace faster than they may have intended at that stage of the run. Once again, the basic principles of self-discipline, patience and pace control have been lost in needless panic and the penalty begins to apply itself around the halfway mark when the runner suddenly realises that he or she is already running out of steam or into physical discomfort that should not be evident for at least another 10 or 15 kilometres.

It is the same with the marathoner who is passed by runners who look older. What an insult, what an indignity, is the thought that flashes through the mind and the sucker quickens pace to keep up with them. It might well be that they are already running too fast themselves and he or she has fallen into the same trap. How much wiser it would have been, is the later thought, if I had stayed at my pace, the pace I could handle, and had the pleasure of catching and passing them some kilometres down the road.

In fact, unless you are an elite runner in your age group, your first and only rival in a marathon should be yourself, at least until you get close to the finish and are in such a comfortable and confident state that you can have a crack at burning off a few of those immediately in front of you.

In the shorter events, if you have plenty of stamina and need to use your endurance to have a chance of winning, it is sometimes worth the gamble to make the early pace fast. But the wind must not be too strong and you have to hope that the faster runners will be foolish enough to follow. If they are experienced, they probably won't; they'll be holding back and relying on using their superior speed in the closing stages to bring you down. Your best hope now is that you'll be able to take a breather without getting caught and then speed up again.

Getting to know your opposition as much as you can isn't easy in big masters' fields but you keep notes of what you do find out for future reference. It's all part of the fun and excitement of the chase.

Always remember that the shortest way to the finish is on the inside track and on the inside of road and cross-country bends and corners. Every time you run outside others on bends and curves, you are adding to the distance you have to run. The only time you should move out is for passing other runners or positioning yourself for your final kick.

In 800-metre races, runners cover the first 300 metres in lanes and then the outer lane runners cut straight across towards the inside. They lose six metres or more. What they should do is aim for the far inside corner and run directly to it, saving those six metres or so for the end of the race.

Runners often put in bursts from positions in the middle of the field, take up another trailing position and then drift back again. It is wasted effort.

Every time you make a move, it should have some purpose in it and, once you have achieved that purpose, you must not let it go again.

Running history is full of stories of athletes who should have run better and they are all valuable lessons for the diligent student of tactics. Every time you finish a race, analyse what you did wrong as well as what you did right. It is particularly important to consider whether you ran to your pre-race plan, whether it worked and, if it didn't, to determine why it didn't.

A classic example of how to fox the opposition occurred in the 1964 Olympic Games steeplechase in Tokyo, won by Belgium's Gaston Roelants. He was noted for starting fast and running his opponents into the ground early. But in the Tokyo semi-finals, Roelants noticeably began to tire and did not look as fit as he had previously.

When the final field lined up two days later and the gun was fired, Roelants didn't go to the front as he usually did and was expected to do. It was apparent the other runners were confused by this and were at a loss about what to do. So, instead of the fast early pace, everyone muddled along. No one was prepared to force the pace.

With 1,000 metres gone, Roelants suddenly jumped into the lead and began running as he usually did at the beginning of a race. The rest were taken completely by surprise and let him get away to a good lead he held until the finish.

It seemed to me that Roelants had realised that if he ran his usual front race, making it harder for everyone else, he would tire before the finish; but he calculated that he could last out a fast 2,000 metres and so re-planned his front-running race from there. His rivals neither anticipated this switch of tactics nor could counter it.

When Murray Halberg reached the final of the 5000 metres at the 1960 Olympics in Rome, we knew from our study of the opposition that there was only one way he could win it — by jumping the field with three laps to go and running himself out to stay in front.

This theory was based on a discovery I made during my early years of developing my system: that if I trained for the 5,000 m by preparing over

10,000 m and 1500 m, it did not necessarily mean that I would run a good 5,000 m. I had to accustom myself to the actual speed required over that distance. Hence the use of time trials in my schedules. Most 5,000 m runners are one of two types: the natural 1,500 m runner or the 10,000 m runner. The 1,500 man finds the early pace well within his compass and in the nervous tension of a big race may be inclined to go fast too early. Between, say 2,800 m and 3,500 m, he will begin to tire. The 10,000 man, a stayer, finds the early speed difficult to cope with and, about the time the 1,500 m man is beginning to sag, is beginning to wonder if he can maintain that speed to the finish.

So, in most of these 5,000 m races, there is a general moment of indecision and reluctance. The pace slackens and falters; no one, except a trained and alert 5,000 m runner like Halberg was, is prepared to go. That is the psychological moment to strike and that is why Halberg went. Observant coaches and runners should have anticipated it because we pulled the same break with Halberg in the three miles in the Commonwealth Games in Cardiff two years earlier.

The last time I won the New Zealand marathon title in Auckland, is used the weather tactically to beat my opposition. The pre-race favourite, Bill Richards, came from the much-cooler southern city of Christchurch and race day in Auckland was marked by typically high humidity.

This was 1955 and Richards had run 2:30, which was great running in those days and he as full of confidence, but I reasoned the Auckland heat would get to him if I aided and abetted it. So I cracked on the pace for three or four miles, dragging the field after me, and then eased back out of it. The chance I took paid off. With six miles left, I was seventh and Richards was about a mile ahead. But I was fresher than he was and I was able to run the last mile in five minutes while he struggled over it in eight. I passed him and finished the last lap to the finish before he began it. The early speed had drained his reserves and then the heat and humidity had completely beaten him down.

There is another lesson in there. If you are confident you are going to be difficult to beat, keep the information to yourself. Catch the opposition by surprise; don't tell them what to expect so they can prepare an answer before the gun goes.

Before the 1974 Commonwealth Games 10,000 metres in Christchurch, all the spotlights were focussed on the great Dave Bedford, of England, a seasoned runner at the distance.

My man, Richard Tayler, had a best 10,000 m time of only 28:24 but he had just run a 5,000 m time trial with consummate ease in 13:40 and it was apparent to us he was going to be difficult to beat. He could run a 2:15 marathon and a sub-four mile, so he had both the speed and the stamina. But we kept the time trial information and the rest of the theory to ourselves and let Bedford have his time in the sun.

Knowing Bedford like front-running and that the Africans in the field would probably be up there too, I guessed a fair amount of jostling would occur so I told Tayler to sit back and wait till the field settled down and some of the leaders had dropped off the pace.

Bedford and the other British runner, Black, both got tangled up with the Africans, with Black getting several body checks which seemed to upset Bedford more than Black. At the 5,000 m mark, Tayler was about 60 metres behind the leaders. He looked right out of contention but, as the early pace took its toll, he gradually closed up on the four leaders. With two laps to go, Bedford and the others were spent forces and Black suddenly took off.

It was perfect. Tayler had better speed than Black and fine endurance as well— he beat Black comfortably by about 60 metres, with a sustained sprint over the last 300 metres, and set a Commonwealth record of 27:46, his best time by about 40 seconds.

In the 1964 Olympics, in Tokyo, I had two men in the final, Peter Snell and John Davies. Snell already had the 800 m gold medal for the second time and was hot favourite to win again but we reasoned that Davies could not make a place if it came down to a sprint finish because his speed was not good enough. There were many faster men in the field.

Davies had tried a sprint finish in the semi-finals from about 250 m and had nearly given me heart failure because everyone else had the same idea and he was four lanes wide on the final bend, trying to outsprint faster men.

Somehow, he scrambled fourth to qualify but we didn't want that to happen again so we decided that, with 800 m to go in the final, Davies would take over the pace and Snell would take up a place by his shoulder. He was a long-striding runner and would be difficult to pass and anyone trying would be forced two or three lanes wide.

At first, everything happened as if we had told all the others what to do. France's Michell Bernard led, as we had expected, and Davies sat back on the danger-man, Dyrol Burleson, of America, ahead of the rest. At 700 metres, Bernard began to flag, as expected, and Davies quickly took over. But, before Snell could get up on the outside, another runner nabbed the place we had reserved for him.

With 250 left, Snell was boxed in. He should have dropped back and gone round the field as he did in the semi-final but instead stuck his right arm out like a traffic signal and the Englishman John Whetton obligingly gave him a gap. Snell was off and away with Davies sprinting as hard as he could. Into the straight, Whetton ran round him, forcing him to change course and slow a little, just enough to let the Czech Josef Odlozil pip him for second.

These tactics worked because we knew the runners we were competing against as well as the type of training they used. Bernard, for instance, was never a real threat because he was interval-trained and we knew he couldn't last three hard races as my two could. Snell actually ran the last 400 m in 53.2 seconds and the last 300 in 38.6.

Be careful in track races. Pass other runners only in the straights unless there is no option but to pass on a bend. Hug that pole line as much as possible; the further you stray from it, the longer the race becomes.

Try to keep the pace as even and economical as possible; mid-race sprints and surges lessen the likelihood you'll be sprinting at the end.

Go into every race with a plan in mind. Whether the race goes according to that plan depends on many factors but, if you consider all the possibilities, use logic and judge your own tactics well, you will not be surprised by others' tactics and can quite often call the tune.

15 CROSS-COUNTRY TRAINING

For all athletes, cross-country training is of great benefit as a general conditioner. Because the ground you run on is usually uneven and undulating, leg muscles and tendons are subjected to various resistances not met on even surfaces. They are often stretched to greater extremes, which adds suppleness and strength. For instance, of soft ground, heels and toes sink deeper, giving the ankles a greater range of movement, which steadily improves flexibility. Ankle strength and flexibility are important developments in running and cross-country running is one of the best ways of helping that development.

Athletes who run with stiff upper body muscles or use an exaggerated leg-driving action learn to relax and move more economically by cross-country training and racing. If you're one of them, get out on muddy, sandy or soft ground where it is difficult to gain good footing and traction. You will soon learning that driving hard on these surfaces consumes energy and is extremely tiring.

You will also learn that the solution is to relax the upper body muscles, keep the arm action low, hold the hips forward and develop a pulling action rather than a driving one. The effort of forward movement will be reduced to a minimum.

Poorly conditioned runners are inclined to tighten their upper body muscles and hold their arms high. The faults grow worse as they get more tired so the running becomes even more inefficient. They need the discipline of relaxation and going with the terrain that cross-country training encourages.

The hilly terrains of cross-country courses have another value. Hill running offers resistance, adding a further dimension to the encouragement of ankle flexibility.

Running uphill develops power and ankle suppleness, which will induce a more driving, natural stride. The steeper the hills, the more the ankle and leg muscles will have to flex.

Heavily-built runners will find uphill running more difficult, because they'll need more energy to lift their bodyweight against gravity; but even if they are forced to struggle in the beginning, they will climb to added speed, power and muscular endurance.

Uphill running forces you to lift your knees higher, which is one of the most desirable developments for runners, as knee lift governs stride length and speed. It also develops the muscle fibres, both red and white, which increases power.

Lightweights usually beat heavyweights over hill cross-country and track steeplechase courses but this should not discourage the heavier runners because everyone gains from the exercise. I have invariably found that the runners who don't like cross-country running are the ones who need it most but find it most difficult to handle. The cause is usually poor and uneconomical technique and they need perseverance to overcome their faults. It will pay in the long run.

Training over country, on forest trails, around golf courses and parks has important psychological value, because you tend to run in these environments in a non-pressured way, speeding up and slowing down according to the lay of the land, the conditions and your personal reactions – even slowing to admire a particular view doesn't challenge the conscience.

Accurate timing is impossible so you tend to run at speeds that make you pleasantly tired rather than leave you exhausted. The pace is often near your best aerobic speed but you achieve it in a relaxed frame of mind. Anaerobic running over country only occurs during some form of fartlek training and that is used only when the runner is in a more advanced stage of physical fitness.

Cross-country racing doesn't have the nervous tensions and sustained speed running of track and road racing, so the overload tends to be on the muscular system, easing pressure on the cardiac system. This reduces the oxygen debt and allows for reasonable rather than excessive states of fatigue.

Nevertheless, although you can slack off at times, knowing that no one is watching because you are out of sight of any spectators, the disciplinary factor is good. You subconsciously control your effort to be more economical and this can only be good for your general development.

Cross-country will emphasise the value of calisthenics and suppling and stretching exercises. These help in handling fences, hurdles and other obstacles. The first time you meet these challenges, they may look forbidding but, with practice, you can develop your technique to take them comfortably and even look forward to them.

Vaults can be one-handed or two-handed, depending on the obstacle's height and the ground conditions approaching it. It is also advisable to practise rolling under wire fences. It might be a messy method but it is often faster, easier and safer than climbing them. So jumping, vaulting, hurdling and rolling are all necessary arts for the keen cross-country runner.

With high knees and relaxed arm action, Magee strides towards the camera.

16 TRAINING TERMS

A number of terms have already been used and more will follow in the schedules, so this is to explain them to you more clearly.

Aerobic training means running within your capacity to use oxygen. This differs from one person to another but everyone can increase capacity through exercise. The limit in using oxygen this way is known as the maximum steady state, or aerobic threshold.

Anaerobic training means you are exercising without sufficient oxygen. You have exceeded the steady state. This is possible through chemical changes in your metabolism. It is an uneconomic way of exercising because great oxygen debts can build up which quickly produce waste products, such as lactic acid, and lead to neuro muscular breakdown. The tired muscles just refuse to function. Proper training can develop your aerobic capacity to handle an oxygen debt of approximately 15 to 20 litres when you move into anaerobic exercise, which is a necessary part of your training.

Muscular conditioning and strength give you the ability to exert a single explosive force against an object. This is a vital factor in contact sports, which many masters still play with a great deal of zest and competitiveness. It involves weight training, which should be done only under expert guidance, should be done regularly and should make sure that opposing muscle groups are properly balanced.

It has been found that the maximum training effect is achieved by using only 40 to 50 per cent of the maximum strength in voluntary isometric muscle contractions. Muscle strength is gradually lost when less than 20 per cent of muscle strength is used.

You do not train to the point of complete muscular fatigue to stimulate increased strength. A maximum isometric contraction for one or two seconds is enough to provide a training stimulus, but the time should be increased to between four to six seconds when the contraction involves only two-thirds of the maximum. Very short contractions have no effect.

Once a day is sufficient. The muscles will not respond to further stimulus on the same day. It seems that stimulus every second day will increase strength about 80 per cent, twice a week about 60 per cent, and once a week only 40 per cent. One training stimulus every fourteen days produces no change at all in muscular strength.

The muscles that show the least increase among all exercised groups are those used most strenuously in day-to-day activities. An atrophied muscle group, under training stimulus, shows a rate of increase in strength five or six times as great as a normal untrained muscle given the same stimulus.

Muscular endurance is the quality which enables muscles to maintain contractions in conditions of fatigue, or the ability to continue work and postpone and tolerate fatigue, and this is the important factor in running training.

In **developing speed**, there are three running exercises you must consider to improve knee lift, ankle flexibility and power, and to learn to run tall by keeping upward. In effect, lifting the upper body off the pelvis.

Sprinting speed is best improved by developing the running technique of the athlete, which involves perfect co-ordination. Again, in team field sports this is an important factor. Cricket, for example, needs a fast take-off when fielding and batting and that means some understanding of sprint techniques and conditioning to put the technique into effect.

A typical sprint workout: warm-up by running easily for seven minutes, then spend eight minutes doing two or three stride-outs over 60 metres, suppling and stretching with exercises until you feel loose. Then, with three-minute intervals between runs, go twice through these exercises over 100 metres:

Keeping the upper body as relaxed as possible, move your legs as fast as you can with a high knee-lifting action, keeping on your toes throughout and keeping the back leg straight. Forward progress should be slow.

Now run with a bounding action and a good knee lift, concentrating on working the ankles hard. Drive hard with each stride. This exercise is best on an upward slope.

Run tall by keeping high on your toes and lifting the body upwards as you run.

Try combining all these actions while running fast and then cool down with a 15-minute jog.

Time trials are to develop co-ordination in your running, not to set records. So run them at less than full effort, trying to maintain an even pace, and do not sprint at the end.

The marathon schedule includes a 35 km trial run four weeks before the marathon you intend to tackle. This is also for co-ordination, for pace judgment, for putting your finger on any factors that are not quite right. It is important to keep the pace on the level you intend to use in the marathon.

This trial has another important benefit; your condition, if you run the trial sensibly, it will take a leap forward about ten days later which might surprise you.

Another view of uphill running drills, showing the high front knee lift, the

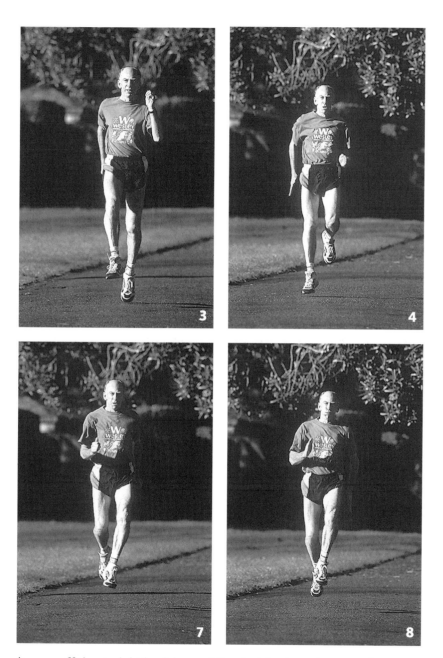

bounce off the straight back leg and the straight-through arm action.

17 THE SCHEDULES

Remember: These schedules are guidelines only for achieving maximum performance. As we discussed earlier, listen to your body because you will not always be in the mood to do precisely what the schedule recommends on any given day.

MIDDLE DISTANCE

	For six to 12 weeks
Monday:	Long aerobic running 1/4 to 1 hour
Tuesday:	Long aerobic running 1 to 1 1/2 hours
Wednesday:	Easy fartlek running 3/4 to 1 hour
Thursday:	Long aerobic running 1 to 1 1/2 hours
Friday:	Long aerobic running 1/2 to 1 hour
Saturday:	Long aerobic running 1 hour
Sunday:	Long aerobic running 1 to 2 hours

	For four weeks
Monday:	Time trial 3 km
Tuesday:	Hill springing and bounding, steep hill or steps running 1/2 to 1 hour
Wednesday:	Relaxed striding 200 m by eight to ten times
Thursday:	Hill springing and bounding, steep hill or steps running 1/2 to 1 hour
Friday:	Jogging 1/2 hour
Saturday:	Hill springing and bounding, steep hill or steps running 1/2 to 1 hour
Sunday:	Jogging 1 to 2 hours

For two weeks

Monday:	Repetitions 800 m by three to six times
Tuesday:	Hill springing and bounding 1/2 to 3/4 hour
Wednesday:	Time trial 3 km
Thursday:	Sprint training
Friday:	Jogging 1/2 hour
Saturday:	Repetitions 200 m by eight to ten times
Sunday:	Jogging 1 to 2 hours

For two weeks

Monday:	Repetitions 1,000 m by three to five times
Tuesday:	Easy fartlek running 1/2 to 3/4 hour
Wednesday:	Time trial 3 km
Thursday:	Fast relaxed running 100 m by eight to ten times
Friday:	Jogging 1/2 hour
Saturday:	Repetitions 200 m by eight to ten times
Sunday:	Jogging 1 to 2 hours

800 AND 1500 METRES

For one week each

Monday:	100 m wind sprint every 200 m by six to ten times
Tuesday:	Easy fartlek running 3/4 to 1 hour
Wednesday:	Time trials 200 m and 600 m
Thursday:	Fast relaxed running 100 m by ten times
Friday:	Jogging 1/2 hour
Saturday:	Time trial 1,500 m
Sunday:	Jogging 1 1/2 hours

Monday:	100 m wind sprint every 200 m six to ten times
Tuesday:	Easy fartlek running 3/4 hour
Wednesday:	Time trials 200 m and 1,000 m
Thursday:	Fast relaxed running 100 m by ten times
Friday:	Jogging 1/2 hour
Saturday:	Time trial 1,500 m
Sunday:	Jogging 1 1/2 hours

Monday:	100 m wind sprint every 200 m by six to ten times
Tuesday:	Easy fartlek running 3/4 hour
Wednesday:	Time trials 200 m and 600 m
Thursday:	Fast relaxed running 100 m by ten times
Friday:	Jogging 1/2 hour
Saturday:	Time trial 600 m
Sunday:	Jogging 1 1/2 hours

Monday:	100 m wind sprint every 200 m eight to ten times
Tuesday:	Easy fartlek running 3/4 hour
Wednesday:	Time trials 200 m and 1,000 m
Thursday:	Fast relaxed running 100 m by ten times
Friday:	Jogging 1/2 hour
Saturday:	Time trial 1,500 m
Sunday:	Jogging 1 hour

Monday:	45 m wind sprint every 100 m by sixteen times
Tuesday:	Easy fartlek running 1/2 hour
Wednesday:	Time trials 200 m and 1,200 m
Thursday:	Fast relaxed running 100 m by six to eight times
Friday:	Jogging 1/2 hour
Saturday:	Time trial 600 m
Sunday:	Jogging 1 hour

Monday:	45 m wind sprint every 100 m by twelve times
Tuesday:	Easy fartlek running 1/2 hour
Wednesday:	Time trial 400 m
Thursday:	Fast relaxed running 100 m by six times
Friday:	Jogging 1/2 hour
Saturday:	THE RACE 800 m or 1,500 m
Sunday:	Jogging 1 hour

5 KM OR 10 KM

For last six weeks (one week each)

Monday:	100 m wind sprint every 200 m by eight to ten times
Tuesday:	Easy fartlek running 3/4 to 1 hour
Wednesday:	Time trials 200 m and 1,000 m
Thursday:	Fast relaxed running 100 m by ten times
Friday:	Jogging 1/2 hour
Saturday:	Time trial 5 km
Sunday:	Jogging 1 to 1 1/2 hours

Monday:	100 m wind sprint every 200 m by five to ten times
Tuesday:	Easy fartlek running 3/4 to 1 hour
Wednesday:	Time trials 200 m and 800 m
Thursday:	Fast relaxed running 100 m by twelve times
Friday:	Jogging 1/2 hour
Saturday:	Time trial 10 km
Sunday:	Jogging 1 to 1 1/2 hours

Monday:	100 m wind sprint every 200 m by eight to ten times
Tuesday:	Easy fartlek running 3/4 to 1 hour
Wednesday:	Time trials 200 m and 1,000 m
Thursday:	Fast relaxed running 100 m by ten times
Friday:	Jogging 1/2 hour
Saturday:	Time trial 5 km
Sunday:	Jogging 1 to 1 1/2 hours

Monday:	100 m wind sprint every 200 m by eight to ten times
Tuesday:	Easy fartlek running 3/4 to 1 hour
Wednesday:	Time trials 200 m and 3,000 m
Thursday:	Fast relaxed running 100m by twelve times
Friday:	Jogging 1/2 hour
Saturday:	Time trial 10 km
Sunday:	Jogging 1 hour

Monday:	45 m wind sprint every 100 m by sixteen times
Tuesday:	Easy fartlek running 1/2 hour
Wednesday:	Time trials 200 m and 3,000 m
Thursday:	Fast relaxed running 100 m by six times
Friday:	Jogging 1/2 hour
Saturday:	Time trial 5 km
Sunday:	Jogging 1 hour

Monday:	45 m wind sprint every 100 m by twelve times
Tuesday:	Easy fartlek running 1/2 hour
Wednesday:	Time trial 1,600 m
Thursday:	Jogging 1/2 hour
Friday:	Jogging 1/2 hour
Saturday:	RACE
Sunday:	Jogging 1 hour

CONTINUATION OF RACING

Monday:	Jogging 1 hour
Tuesday:	45 m wind sprint every 100 m by six to eight times
Wednesday:	Time trials 200 m and 600 m
Thursday:	Fast relaxed running 100 m by eight to ten times
Friday:	Jog 1/2 hour
Saturday:	RACE
Sunday:	Jogging 1 to 1 1/2 hours

MARATHON

	For four weeks
Monday:	Jogging 30 to 45 minutes
Tuesday:	Jogging 45 to 60 minutes
Wednesday:	Jogging 30 to 45 minutes
Thursday:	Jogging 45 to 60 minutes
Friday:	Jogging 30 minutes
Saturday:	Jogging 45 minutes
Sunday:	Jogging 60 minutes

	For two weeks
Monday:	Long aerobic running 30 to 45 minutes
Tuesday:	Jogging 60 to 75 minutes
Wednesday:	Long aerobic running 30 to 45 minutes
Thursday:	Jogging 60 to 75 minutes
Friday:	Jogging 30 minutes
Saturday:	Long aerobic running 30 to 45 minutes
Sunday	Jogging 60 to 90 minutes

	For four weeks
Monday:	Easy fartlek running 30 to 45 minutes
Tuesday:	Long aerobic running 45 to 75 minutes
Wednesday:	Easy fartlek running 30 to 45 minutes
Thursday:	Long aerobic running 45 to 75 minutes
Friday:	Relaxed striding 150 m by four to six times
Saturday:	Easy fartlek running 45 to 60 minutes
Sunday:	Long aerobic running 60 to 120 minutes

For four weeks

Monday:	Hill springing and bounding, steep hill or steps running 30 to 45 minutes
Tuesday:	Long aerobic running 45 to 75 minutes
Wednesday:	Easy fartlek running 30 to 45 minutes
Thursday:	Hill springing and bounding, steep hill or steps running 30 to 45 minutes
Friday:	Relaxed striding 200 m by four to six times
Saturday:	Hill springing and bounding, steep hill or steps running 30 minutes
Sunday:	Long aerobic running 60 to 120 minutes

One week

Monday:	Repetitions 800 m by two to four times
Tuesday:	Long aerobic running 45 to 75 minutes
Wednesday:	Time trial 3,000 m
Thursday:	Long aerobic running 45 to 75 minutes
Friday:	Relaxed striding 200 m by four to six times
Saturday:	Time trial 5,000 m
Sunday:	Long aerobic running 90 to 120 minutes

One week

Monday:	Repetitions 1,000 m by two or three times
Tuesday:	Long aerobic running 60 to 90 minutes
Wednesday:	Time trial 5,000 m
Thursday:	Long aerobic running 60 to 75 minutes
Friday:	Relaxed striding 200 m by four to six times
Saturday:	Time trial 10,000 m
Sunday:	Long aerobic running 90 to 120 minutes

One week

Monday:	Repetitions 1,500 m by two or three times
Tuesday:	Long aerobic running 60 to 90 minutes
Wednesday:	Time trial 5,000 m
Thursday:	Long aerobic running 60 to 90 minutes
Friday:	Relaxed striding 200 m by four to six times
Saturday:	Time trial 5,000 m
Sunday:	Long aerobic running 90 to 120 minutes

One week

Monday:	Repetitions 800 m by three to five times
Tuesday:	Long aerobic running 60 to 90 minutes
Wednesday:	Time trial 3,000 m
Thursday:	Easy fartlek running 45 minutes
Friday:	Relaxed striding 200 m by four to six times
Saturday:	Time trial 10,000 m
Sunday:	Long aerobic running 90 to 120 minutes

One week

Monday:	100 m wind sprint every 200 m by six to eight times
Tuesday:	Jogging 60 to 90 minutes
Wednesday:	Time trial 5,000 m
Thursday:	Jogging 60 to 90 minutes
Friday:	High knee-lift exercise 100 m by six times
Saturday:	Time trial 3,000 m
Sunday:	Jogging 60 to 90 minutes

One week

Monday:	100 m wind sprint every 200 m by six times
Tuesday:	Jogging 60 minutes
Wednesday:	Time trial 2,000 m
Thursday:	Jogging 45 minutes
Friday:	Jogging 30 minutes
Saturday:	Time trial 35 km - fast!
Sunday:	Jogging 30 to 45 minutes

One week

Monday:	Jogging 45 to 60 minutes
Tuesday:	Jogging 45 to 60 minutes
Wednesday:	Relaxed striding 200 m by six times
Thursday:	Easy fartlek running 30 minnutes
Friday:	Jogging 30 minutes
Saturday:	Time trial 3,000 metres
Sunday:	Jogging 120 minutes

One week

Monday:	100 m wind sprint every 200 m by six to eight times
Tuesday:	Jogging 60 to 90 minutes
Wednesday:	Time trial 3,000 m
Thursday:	Jogging 60 to 90 minutes
Friday:	Jogging 30 minutes
Saturday:	Time trial 10,000 m
Sunday:	Jogging 90 to 120 minutes

	One week
Monday:	100 m wind sprint every 200 m by six to eight times
Tuesday:	Jogging 60 to 90 minutes
Wednesday:	Time trial 5,000 m
Thursday:	Easy fartlek running 30 to 45 minutes
Friday:	Jogging 30 minutes
Saturday:	Time trial 3,000 m
Sunday:	Jogging 45 to 60 minutes

	One week
Monday:	Fast relaxed running 100 m by six times
Tuesday:	Time trial 2,000 m
Wednesday:	Jogging 45 minutes
Thursday:	Jogging 30 minutes
Friday:	Jogging 30 minutes
Saturday:	MARATHON RACE
Sunday:	Jog easily for at least one week.

The following schedule is for continuation racing after you have peaked for the first one you wanted to do your best in. It has been tested for all distances, including cross-country racing, which is another field in which masters are appearing in growing numbers. It is ideal for keeping fun runners in trim for continued running throughout the fun run season.

Non-Race Week

Monday:	Repetitions 1,500 m by three or 800 m by six
Tuesday:	Aerobic running 60 to 90 minutes
Wednesday:	Time trial 2,000 or 3,000 m
Thursday:	Aerobic running 60 to 90 minutes
Friday:	Fast relaxed striding 100 m by ten times
Saturday:	Time trial 200 or 3,000 m
Sunday:	Aerobic running 90 minutes or more

Race Week

Monday:	Wind sprint 100 m every 200 m by six to ten times
Tuesday:	Easy fartlek running 45 to 60 minutes
Wednesday:	Time trial 1,600 or 2,400 m
Thursday:	Fast relaxed striding 100 m by six times
Friday:	Jog 30 minutes
Saturday:	Race
Sunday:	Aerobic running 90 minutes or more

Our Programme

Jozef Sneyers
Soccer Training
An Annual Programme

ISBN 1-84126-017-7
c. DM 34 ,-/SFr 31,60/ÖS 248,-
£ 12.95/US$ 19.95
Austr.$ 29.95/Can$ 29.95

Gerhard Frank
**Soccer Training
Programmes**

ISBN 3-89124-556-4
DM 29,80/SFr 27,70/ÖS 218,-
£ 12.95/US$ 17.95
Austr.$ 29.95/Can$ 25.95

Ilona E. Gerling
**Teaching Children's
Gymnastics**

ISBN 3-89124-549-1
DM 29,80/SFr 27,70/ÖS 218,-
£ 12.95/US $ 17.95
Austr.$ 29.95/Can$ 25.95

Bischops/Gerards
Soccer
Warming-up and Cooling down

ISBN 1-84126-014-2
c. DM 24,80/SFr 23,-/ÖS 181,-
£ 8.95/US$ 14.95
Austr.$24.95/Can$ 20.95

Bischops/Gerards
Junior Soccer:
A Manual for Coaches

ISBN 1-84126-000-2
DM 29,80/SFr 27,70/ÖS 218,-
£ 12.95/US$ 17.95
Austr.$ 29.95/Can$ 25.95

Thomas Kaltenbrunner
Contact Improvisation

ISBN 3-89124-485-1
DM 29,80/SFr 27,70/ÖS 218,-
£ 12.95/US$ 17.95
Austr.$ 29.95/Can$ 25.95

Bischops/Gerards
Soccer •
One-On-One

ISBN 1-84126-013-4
c. DM 24,80/SFr 23,-/ÖS 181,-
£ 8.95/US$ 14.95
Austr.$24.95/Can$ 20.95

Bischops/Gerards
**Coaching Tips for
Children's Soccer**

ISBN 3-89124-529-7
DM 14,80/SFr 14,40/ÖS 108,-
£ 5.95/US$ 8.95
Austr.$ 14.95/Can$ 12.95

Dörte Wessel-Therhorn
Jazz Dance Training

ISBN 3-89124-499-1
DM 29,80/SFr 27,70/ÖS 218,-
£ 12.95/US$ 17.95
Austr.$ 29.95/Can$ 25.95

Gerhard Frank
Soccer •
Creative Training

ISBN 1-84126-015-0
c. DM 24,80/SFr 23,-/ÖS 181,-
£ 8.95/US$ 14.95
Austr.$24.95/Can$ 20.95

Pieter/Heijmans
**Scientific Coaching for
Olympic Taekwondo**

ISBN 3-89124-389-8
DM 29,80/SFr 27,70/ÖS 218,-
£ 12.95/US$ 17.95
Austr.$ 29.95/Can$ 25.95

Bergmann/Butz
**Adventure Sports –
Big Foot**

ISBN 3-89124-497-5
DM 34 ,-/SFr 31,60/ÖS 248,-
£ 14.95/US$ 19.95
Austr.$ 29.95/Can$ 29.95

Erich Kollath
Soccer •
Techniques & Tactics

ISBN 1-84126-016-9
c. DM 24,80/SFr 23,-/ÖS 181,-
£ 8.95/US$ 14.95
Austr.$24.95/Can$ 20.95

Rudolf Jakhel
**Modern Sports
Karate**

ISBN 3-89124-428-2
DM 29,80/SFr 27,70/ ÖS 218,-
£ 12.95/US$ 17.95
Austr.$ 29.95/Can$ 25.95

Münch/ Mund
Straight Golf

ISBN 3-89124-503-3
DM 34,-/SFr 31,60/ÖS 248,-
£ 12.95/US$ 19.95
Austr.$ 29.95/Can$ 25.95

• In preparation

MEYE
&MEYE
SPORT

Our Programme

Our Programme

Gudrun Paul
Aerobic Training ●

ISBN 1-84126-021-5
DM 29,80/SFr 27,70/ÖS 218,-
£ 12.95/US$ 17.95
Austr.$ 29.95/Can$ 25.95

Unger/Rössler
**Bodywork –
Power for Women** ●

ISBN 1-84126-022-3
DM 29,80/SFr 27,70/ÖS 218,-
£ 12.95/US$ 17.95
Austr.$ 29.95/Can$ 25.95

Diel/Menges
Surfing ●
In search of the perfect wave

ISBN 1-84126-023-1
DM 29.80/SFr 27,70/ÖS 218,-
£ 12.95/US $ 17.95
Austr. $ 29.95/Can $ 25.95

Wolfgang Fritsch
Rowing ●

ISBN 1-84126-024-X
DM 34 ,-/SFr 31,60/ÖS 248,-
£ 14.95/US$ 19.95
Austr.$ 29.95/Can$ 29.95

Green/Hardman (eds.)
**Physical Education
A Reader**

ISBN 3-89124-463-0
DM 39,80/SFr 37,-/ÖS 291,-
£ 17.95/US $ 29,-
Austr.$ 37.95/ Can$ 39.95

Arthur Lydiard revolutionised the training of middle and long distance runners in the 1960s. Since then his methods have contributed to the success of countless athletes around the world, including four time Olympic gold medalist and world record setter Lasse Viren of Finland.

Lydiard/Gilmour
**Distance Training for
Women Athletes**

ISBN 1-84126-002-9
DM 24,80/SFr 23,-/ÖS 181,-
£ 9.95/US$ 14.95
Austr.$ 24.95/Can$ 20.95

Lydiard Gilmour
**Distance Training for
Masters**

ISBN 1-84126-018-5
c. DM 29,80/SFr 27,70/ÖS 218,-
£ 12.95/US$ 17.95
Austr.$ 29.95/Can$ 25.95

Lydiard/Gilmour
**Distance Training for
Young Athletes**

ISBN 3-89124-533-5
DM 29,80/SFr 27,70/ÖS 218,-
£ 12.95/US$ 17.95
Austr.$ 29.95/Can$ 25.95

Arthur Lydiard
Running to the Top

ISBN 3-89124-440-1
DM 29,80/SFr 27,70/ÖS 218,-
£ 12.95/US$ 17.95
Austr.$ 29.95/Can$ 25.95

Do you want to improve your training? – Let Lydiard be your personal coach!
For US$ 240,- /year only Lydiard offers you personal training plans and advice.

For more information turn to

www.lydiard.com

or

www.meyer-meyer-sports.com

MEYEᖴ
&MEYE
SPORᎢ

Please order our catalogue!